"It could h̶̶̶̶̶̶̶̶̶̶̶̶̶̶̶̶̶̶̶̶̶̶̶̶̶ know—slip̶̶̶̶̶̶̶̶̶̶̶̶̶̶̶̶̶̶̶̶̶ brakes."

"It wasn't." Her voice was flat, unequivocal.

Michael gave her another glance, this one of curiosity. "What makes you so positive?"

"The look on that guy's face; it was so intent. Like he was in complete control and he knew he was going to hit somebody."

Michael's hands tightened on the steering wheel. Excitement zapped through him. It took tremendous effort to keep his voice quiet and steady. "You say you *saw* him? Saw his face?"

"Yes . . . I can draw him."

Michael whispered, "Good Lord." He didn't dare look at her. After all the weeks of suspense and unrelieved tension, day after day of facing the possibility of his own death, was it possible that Brady was about to do what neither he nor the police could? Could this woman with the Madonna smile and witch's eyes finally give his assassin a *face*?

Dear Reader:

We at Silhouette are very excited to bring you this reading Sensation. Look out for the four books which appear in our Silhouette Sensation series every month. These stories will have the high quality you have come to expect from Silhouette, and their varied and provocative plots will encourage you to explore the wonder of falling in love – again and again!

Emotions run high in these drama-filled novels. Greater sensual detail and an extra edge of realism intensify the hero and heroine's relationship so that you cannot help but be caught up in their every change of mood.

We hope you enjoy this Sensation – and will go on to enjoy many more.

We would love to hear your comments and encourage you to write to us:

Jane Nicholls
Silhouette Books
PO Box 236
Thornton Road
Croydon
Surrey
CR9 3RU

KATHLEEN CREIGHTON
In Defence of Love

Silhouette Sensation

First published in Great Britain in 1993 by Silhouette Books, Eton House, 18-24 Paradise Road, Richmond, Surrey TW9 1SR

© Kathleen Modrovich 1987

Silhouette, Silhouette Sensation and Colophon are Trade Marks of Harlequin Enterprises B.V.

ISBN 0 373 58761 9

18-9303

Made and printed in Great Britain

Other novels by Kathleen Creighton

To Pat Teal, and her husband Jack . . .
Since the strongest feelings are best expressed
in simple phrases,
I think I'll just say, "Thank you,"
and leave it at that.

Chapter 1

Remain seated and come to order. This court is still in session."

Presiding Judge Michael A. Snow put a peppermint candy in his mouth and slipped quietly past the bailiff. As he took his place behind the bench he let his gaze move around the courtroom, briefly touching each occupant, identifying, cataloging. His expression appeared impassive, even bored, but under his black judicial robes his heart was a runaway locomotive.

Is he out there somewhere right now? Will it be today? he wondered.

But there were no surprises today. He knew the bailiff, a buxom young woman named, improbably, Amaretto Jones. She was brisk and efficient and brooked no nonsense in her courtroom. He liked her and worked well with her. He knew the stenographer, too—Heidi Schroeder. She'd worked with him many, many times.

There were the defense lawyers—three stout, balding men in dark pinstripes, huddled in last-minute conference with their clients. The Gianelli brothers were resplendent in sharkskin and diamonds, while their alleged co-conspirator in fraud, Tex Arkin, wore his customary western suit, cowboy boots and ten-gallon Stetson. All three looked clean-shaven, scrubbed and positively cherubic.

The assistant D.A. sat alone at his table, thumbing nervously through his notes. The nervousness was an act—Klineschmidt knew his stuff. He also knew there was an advantage in being underestimated.

The jury box was empty, of course; the jurors had been sequestered for the day's proceedings. The spectator seats were sparsely occupied, too, which wasn't surprising; the routine defense motions for dismissal had all the dramatic potential of a Senate filibuster. In spite of that, the press was well represented. By this time Judge Snow knew all of them by sight—Franklin from UPI, Tobin from AP and Washburn from the *Times*. And that deceptively boyish-looking young man with the red hair, the investigative reporter from KXLA who was doing the in-depth series on organized crime in Los Angeles. Kyle Horner—that was his name. He was with the television station's artist, as usual, and her name was... He consulted a list that was partially hidden under his blotter. Oh, yes. Brady.

He felt an unaccustomed twinge of irritation. Hell of an occupation for a young woman. Courtroom artists were all old men, a dying breed in an obsolete profession. What sort of person would waste her time and talent in a job without a future? And he wished somebody would take her in hand and teach her a little clothes sense. Her taste seemed to run exclusively to jeans and boots and gaudy sweaters. Once she'd even worn a denim jacket that had looked as if she'd stolen it from a skid-row bum. He'd swear she had cut the sleeves off the thing herself.

And her hair. She had quite a lot of it, brown, with gold highlights. She wore it long and very curly—whether natural or permed he wouldn't venture to guess—but not the soft wavy curls that looked as if they'd be nice to touch. Her curls had a wild, fierce look, as if she'd combed them wet with her fingers and let them dry untamed. Her only effort at style seemed to consist of pinning quantities of her hair with a clip that sat on the top of her head like a giant plastic butterfly. The effect was ludicrous, but at least it served to keep the curls out of her face.

And she did have a rather arresting face, when it was visible. Michael supposed she might even be considered attractive. Her jaw was too angular, her nose too prominent and her mouth too full for conventional prettiness, but she had flawless olive-toned skin, and the overall effect put him in mind of certain paintings of the Madonna. Except for her eyes. There was nothing Madonna-like about her eyes. They were deep-set, almond-shaped, heavily lashed and very blue. A pale but penetrating blue that he found damned distracting at times. Incredibly, even now...

He shifted abruptly in his chair and addressed a routine query to the battery of defense attorneys. While he listened to the response he rubbed absently at the front of his robe, at a spot just above his belt buckle where his pulse beat steadily. He noted the incipient softness there and felt the slow burn of anger. Another little thing he owed this jerk, whoever he was. He hadn't been able to go to the gym in weeks. He'd have a lot to catch up on when all this was over.

When it's all over.

His anger turned cold with the awareness that for him "over" could mean two very different things.

Over. Damn it, he was forty-two years old. In his prime. He wasn't at all ready for it to be "over." There were too many things he wanted to do, too many things he hadn't seen. He wanted to see Mont St. Michel at dawn and the Parthenon at sunset and St. Mark's Square at high noon. He wanted to climb the bell tower at Notre Dame and afterward enjoy a cup of coffee in a little café on the Left Bank.

And if he could hear Bach played on just one of Europe's great cathedral organs...

Over? Hell, no, not on your life!

Grimly now, the Honorable Michael A. Snow pulled his attention back to the defense attorney's remarks. He couldn't allow this problem to interfere with his responsibilities as a Superior Court judge; that in itself would constitute a personal defeat. And there was nothing to be gained by worrying. The police were quietly sifting through leads. It was only a matter of time.

But as he sat there, listening to the defense's arguments with his customary expression of heavy-lidded ennui, the questions persisted in his mind like obnoxious mosquitoes: is he out there somewhere? Will it be today?

"Drawing his honor again, are we?" Kyle whispered, smirking.

Brady Flynn stuck out her tongue without looking up from the sketch pad on her knee. "Got any better ideas?" she whispered back. "Everybody else has their backs to me."

"*His* back," Kyle corrected, as he'd been doing since high school. It had become an automatic reflex neither of them really noticed anymore. "Don't give me that. You'd draw the judge if Charles Manson was sitting there making faces at you."

Without slowing the firm, quick strokes she was making with the pencil in her right hand, Brady lifted her other hand and tapped the outer corner of her left eye slowly three times. "He has a very interesting face," she murmured placidly, smiling.

Kyle snorted, and in a parody of her gesture deliberately tapped the end of his rather large, freckled nose. "Methinks the lady hath an interest in more than just the Honorable Michael Snow's face."

Brady grinned, lowered her lashes and went on drawing. The exchange of gestures was an old communication between them, shorthand for the clichés "artist's eye" and "nose for news." The debate over the relative merits and reliability of those two traits had been raging since the days when Kyle was a lowly gofer in the station's newsroom and Brady was still just "Sean Flynn's brat." Over the years the argument, which at times had broadened in scope to encompass philosophy, religion, tastes in food and music and their respective love lives, had gradually been distilled down to those two hand signals. Freely translated, they meant, "Buzz off—I know what I'm talking about."

"I'm going to go get a Coke. Want anything?" Kyle stopped halfway through the process of unfolding himself and whispered in Brady's ear. She shook her head, then paused in her sketching long enough to glance up at him.

"We just had a break."

"Yeah, I know, but this stuff is so damn boring I'll go to sleep if I sit here much longer. I don't know how the judge stays awake. If you ask me, I don't think he does. Sure you don't want to join me?" Again Brady shook her head. Kyle grunted, "See you later—have fun," and slipped past her knees.

When he had gone, Brady turned her attention back to the front of the courtroom, where the judge sat with his elbows on the arms of his chair, his hands clasped across the front of his robe, his jaw like rock and his eyelids at half-mast. He did look sleepy, but Brady knew better. She'd seen that expression a thousand times, and at first she would have sworn the man was bored out of his skull and not listening to a word that was being said. But then all at once he'd sit up, or lean forward just a little, and when he began to speak you knew not only that he'd been listening but that his mind had been clicking away like a computer. In a few words he would cut through all the legalese and verbiage and neatly assemble the pertinent facts. He never raised his voice—

sometimes the reporters complained that they couldn't hear
him and wished he'd speak up—but he could be pretty witty
at times. And at other times, brutal. Brady had seen vet-
eran trial lawyers reduced to pale, tight-lipped silence by
Judge Snow's quiet words.

But he could be gentle, too, and compassionate. Brady
had seen him chat with nervous witnesses and traumatized
victims, seen him calm them and sometimes even make them
smile.

She gave her head a shake and stared down at the sketch
in her lap. Oh, yes, from an artist's point of view Judge
Snow did have an interesting face. Thick, dark hair just beginning to go silver at the temples framed a high forehead
and dark, brooding eyes. He had the nose of an aristocrat,
the jaw of a bare-knuckle brawler and the mouth of a poet.
Brady often found herself watching his mouth, fascinated
by the curve of his lips when he smiled—though he didn't
smile often, and when he did it was more in irony than
amusement. When she tried to imagine him really smiling,
even laughing, his head thrown back, mouth open, eyes
alight with mirth or joy, she found that she couldn't do it.
She knew he was only a man, a human being, but his image
was too stately, too awesome. Too *godlike*.

And, if she stopped to think about it, a judge *was* a little
godlike. Such power—his decisions could literally mean life
or death. Brady shivered suddenly, as if touched by a cold
hand. Such *responsibility*. What kind of man must it take,
she wondered, to carry such a burden? Could such a man
afford himself the luxury of joy? Of vulnerability? Maybe,
after all, a judge couldn't afford to be human.

The door to the courtroom opened. Brady turned to look,
thinking it might be Kyle coming back from the cafeteria,
but it was only a sheriff's deputy with a note for the judge.
The defense lawyer's monologue continued as the deputy
stepped up to the gate and handed the folded piece of paper
to the bailiff. The bailiff glanced at the paper and got to her

feet. The judge gave a barely perceptible nod, and the bailiff placed the note in front of him.

Slowly, almost lazily, Snow extended one arm and drew the message toward him. Brady saw his eyes move, his gaze shift downward. His expression didn't change. After a moment he moved his hand again, slowly and carefully pushing the note back to its original position.

"Mr. Bergman," the judge said, interrupting the defense counselor in midsentence, "I'm sorry, but I'm going to have to call a short recess. We'll continue this in fifteen minutes."

And, just like that, he was gone.

In the silence that followed the judge's abrupt departure, Kyle slipped back into the seat beside Brady.

"Hi, did I miss something?"

"I don't know," Brady said absently, staring at the door to the judge's private chambers. "That was strange."

"What was?"

"A deputy just brought in a note for Judge Snow, and after he read it he just got up and left. Called a recess and left, just like that. Well..." Brady stood up and turned to dump her pad and pencils onto the seat she'd just vacated. "I'm going to take a quick run down the hall myself while I've got a chance. Watch my stuff, will you?"

Kyle murmured a sarcastic reply, but Brady was already out the door.

Weird, she thought as she headed for the rest rooms at a half run. Totally weird. Must be some sort of personal emergency, a family crisis, maybe. Funny, she'd never thought of him as having a family—a wife, children. She couldn't recall Judge Snow ever doing anything like this before. She hoped it wasn't anything serious.

Head down, frowning and absorbed by her speculations, Brady ran smack into a solid wall.

At least that was what it felt like. Except that the wall was breathing hard, and it uttered a soft "Damn!" when she crashed into it.

Brady said, "Oof!" or something equally profound, and would have fallen except for the pair of arms that had closed around her.

She said, "Oh—oh, gee, sir. I'm sorry. I didn't see—" and then fell silent. Michael Snow wasn't listening to her, anyway. He was looking over her head, staring intently down the wide hallway, first one way, then the other. His body felt like rock, except that Brady felt his heart beating against her chest like a series of blows from a cruel fist.

It couldn't have been more than a few seconds—a dozen or so of those painful heartbeats—before Brady felt the sigh of an exhalation, and the arms that held her relaxed. As if aware of her existence for the first time, the judge glanced down at her, then put his hands on her arms and moved her a little distance away from him. Her eyes slowly focused on his. They were blue, Brady saw with some surprise, violet near the pupils, darkening almost to black at the outer edges of the irises. They were also bloodshot and deeply shadowed.

"I'm sorry," he said. Then, clearing his throat: "You're bleeding."

Brady realized then that her lower lip was numb. She touched it gingerly, then licked it. "Must have bitten it," she muttered, looking around distractedly, as if a handkerchief or tissue might magically materialize there in the empty hallway. To her very great surprise, she felt fingers touch the side of her face; then the soft, smooth pad of a thumb slid delicately across her tender lip. After that brief touch, the hand dropped with a small gesture of apology.

"I am sorry."

"It's okay. Really. I wasn't looking—"

"My fault entirely. I was...looking for someone. I thought—"

"No, really. I should have—"

"You're the artist," the judge said suddenly. "From the television station. Brady."

"Yes," Brady whispered, surprised that he knew her name.

There was silence, the tight, vibrant kind that seems louder than sirens. The judge's gaze met hers, and his eyes narrowed, deepening the fan of lines at their corners. For a second or two Brady's breath hung in her throat, and then that hard, penetrating stare dropped once again and was veiled by a sweep of dark lashes.

"Well, you'd better see to that lip." His voice was distant, dismissive.

"Yes—I was on my way to the . . . um . . . anyway."

"You should put some ice on it."

"Well," Brady murmured, but the judge had already stepped back through the doorway he'd burst from only moments ago. The door closed after him with a soft shushing sound. Brady stared at it for another moment, then went on down the hall to the rest room.

Weird, she thought again, gingerly exploring her puffy lip with her tongue. Totally weird.

But it was more than that. For some reason her heart was racing hard and fast, as if she'd just had a terrific scare. And she did feel a little frightened, at that, though she didn't exactly know why. She felt frightened, exhilarated and shaken.

She didn't have a clue what was going on or what had just happened to her, but it was definitely a whole lot more than "weird."

"Wouldn't you know," Kyle said in disgust, hunching his shoulders as he gazed at the rain-spattered courthouse steps. "The weather report said only a thirty-percent chance." He glanced at Brady. "You didn't bring an umbrella, either?"

"Are you kidding? I don't pay any attention unless it's at least sixty percent." In the mid-November twilight the city lights made the wet streets sparkle, as if with stars. It looked like a midsummer's sky turned upside down.

"Hey," Kyle said, "why don't we get a bite to eat here, in the cafeteria? Maybe it'll quit before we're through. And if it doesn't . . ."

"We'll just get wet once," Brady agreed, shivering. She was wearing only a lightweight cotton jacket over a sleeveless sweater—not much protection from the chill of a rainy November evening, even in L.A.

While they waited for an express elevator, Kyle kept looking at Brady, then away. About the third time he did that, Brady asked testily, "What's wrong?"

Kyle shrugged. "Just wondering when you're going to tell me what happened to your lip is all."

Brady touched it—a habit she'd already developed—and frowned ruefully. "You wouldn't believe me if I told you."

"Try me."

"I ran into a judge."

"Wha-at?"

At that moment the elevator at the far end dinged imperiously, and they had to run for it. Several other people got on with them, including a tall woman dressed like Hollywood's idea of a gypsy. She was beautiful in a gaunt, exotic way, and she had a black widow spider painted on one cheek. As the elevator doors slid shut, Kyle casually turned so that he was facing the back of the elevator and the other passengers. Brady lifted her eyebrows at him; he shrugged and gazed innocently toward the ceiling.

As they were disembarking on the top floor, Brady nudged him with an elbow and whispered, "What was *that* all about?"

Kyle hunched his shoulders and gave an exaggerated shiver. "I may be just a kid from Nebraska, but my mother didn't raise any stupid children. 'Son...' she said as she was waving goodbye to me at the old railroad crossing. 'Son, I've only got two pieces of advice to give you as you go off to that great big sinful city: don't buy anything from any-body named Slick, and never turn your back on a lady with a spider on her cheek.' "

Brady burst out laughing, then cried "Ow!" and touched her tender lip. Choking, she gasped, "Only in L.A.!"

"Yeah, don't you love this town? Hey, you were going to tell me about your lip. You ran into a *what*?"

"Shh," Brady whispered. The spider-lady was just ahead of them in the cafeteria line. She was explaining to the at-tendant in cultured tones that she spoke seven languages fluently, including Arabic and Polish. The attendant de-lightedly replied that he was Egyptian—small world—and the two exchanged unintelligible phrases.

"Only in L.A.," Brady murmured again. The spider-lady fascinated her. She had beautiful bones and big, haunting eyes, and Brady was itching to draw her. When she got to the dining room she paused, looking for the woman. She finally spotted her at a table near the windows in a nearly deserted section—deserted except for one other diner. Mi-chael Snow was sitting alone in a corner several tables away from the spider-lady, his back to the windows and the rainy darkness beyond.

"Well, well, it seems the man does eat," Kyle said in the dry, slightly sarcastic manner he used to disguise real inter-est. "I guess that means he must be human after all."

"Oh, he's human," Brady muttered, touching the inside of her swollen lip with her tongue.

Kyle gave her a curious glance and drawled, "I don't know, there are just some people you can't quite picture putting on their pants one leg at a time, know what I mean? Like George Washington. Can you really see old George tossing down a pint with the boys at the local tavern? Laughing it up at a dirty joke? Making love? Now you know he had to do those things, right? The man *was* human, fa-therhood of an entire country notwithstanding. But some people you just can't *picture*. They have a certain aura, an image. Like Mount Rushmore.''

"Shut up, Kyle," Brady said softly. She didn't feel like talking anymore, at least not about her strange, brief encounter with Judge Snow. She hauled Kyle, protesting, to a table between the spider-lady and the judge, plunked her tray down and reached for the drawing tablet she always carried in her oversized shoulder bag. For a while her pencil flew across the pages while rain spattered the glass walls of the cafeteria and her cheese enchilada turned to greenish cardboard on her plate.

"No matter how many times I watch you do that, it always blows me away."

Brady looked up and was faintly surprised to see that Kyle had finished eating. He was puffing on a cigarette and watching her through a curl of blue smoke. She turned the tablet around and slid it across the table to him.

"Why?"

Kyle picked up the tablet, studied it for a moment, then put it back on the table. Brady could see it upside down, a series of sketches, poses, facial expressions, emotions. They were moments in time, captured with a few bold lines and imprisoned there in stark black and white. She had clustered them around a larger drawing, a portrait, softly shaded.

"I don't know," Kyle said. "The likeness is more than photographic. It's almost an invasion of privacy. Hey, Brady. Mind if I keep this? She fascinates me."

"Of course not," Brady said, laughing. "But... ahem... you know what black widow spiders do to their mates."

"Strictly human interest," Kyle said loftily, but he grinned as he tore the page from the tablet, folded it carefully and put it in his coat pocket. "If I happen to run into her again, I might get an interview out of her. Never can tell when a good character story'll come in handy."

"Sure," Brady teased, but she knew that Kyle did have other projects in the works besides his series on organized crime. She'd always thought that someday she'd see his name on the list of nominees for the Emmys, and it wasn't hard to picture the spider-lady turning up as a character in a crime series—though whether as villainess or mysterious lady in distress, Brady couldn't decide. She never knew how Kyle's mind was going to work.

"You know," he said now, turning his attention back to Brady's sketchbook, "it just amazes me that you never had any formal training." He began flipping through the tablet, turning pages with his thumb.

"I had the best teacher in the world," Brady said. "Sean..." She stopped, because saying his name still hurt so much. She missed him. Sean Flynn had been working as a commercial artist in the advertising department at the *Times* when the Sirhan Sirhan trial had begun in Los Angeles. The trial had left local television stations with a story of international importance to cover, and no photographers had been allowed in the courtroom. Using artists to cover trials wasn't entirely new, but Sean had been one of the first to go to work for a station on a full-time basis. As a result, Brady had practically grown up in the station's newsroom.

"Yeah," Kyle said, "I know your dad taught you everything he knew, but talent like this you've got to be born with. And I just wish I could understand what the hell you're doing, wasting—"

"Kyle—"

"Wasting it in a courtroom, when—"

"Kyle, don't start!"

"Look, you know you're going to be out of a job pretty soon." He was still flipping through the tablet. "Face it, there aren't too many diehard camera bigots like His Honor over there left in the judiciary—" He interrupted himself with a soundless whistle. "And speaking of His Honor, you have done a few pictures of the man, haven't you?"

Kyle was smirking again, his lecture forgotten. Brady snatched the tablet back and stuffed it into her bag. Kyle met her frown with a look of big-brotherly amusement.

"Hey, that reminds me. You never did finish telling me about your fat lip. You said you ran into a *judge*?"

"Shh." She shifted uncomfortably and took a bite of cold enchilada.

"Who?"

Fully occupied with trying to chew without further damaging her mouth, Brady nodded in the direction of the neighboring table.

"Judge Snow? You're kidding. When? How?"

Brady said dryly, "Not to mention what, where and why." But she didn't really feel like teasing Kyle tonight. The episode was too fresh, and the strange feelings it had left her with still quivered along her nerves. She felt so unsettled. Maybe if she talked about it, if she told Kyle about it, it wouldn't seem so important. It was such a stupid little thing, a little bit embarrassing, a little silly. She leaned forward, her dinner forgotten again. "Kyle, it was the funniest thing—"

"Hold it," Kyle interrupted in an undertone.

Brady followed his gaze, then watched with unabashed interest as the Honorable Michael Snow stood up and prepared to leave. He had his hands full juggling his tray, a briefcase, a raincoat and an umbrella. She realized that he was a very tall man, with that slight stoop tall men often have—the result, she supposed, of always having to bend to be on a level with other people. It was odd seeing him in regular clothes, too—gray slacks and sweater and a sport jacket in a muted plaid.

"Snappy dresser," Kyle commented.

Brady said "Hush," and watched the judge's glance sweep across the spider-lady, touch Kyle with a slight start of recognition and finally come to rest on her. She felt the weight of his gaze like a physical touch.

Suddenly, and very vividly, she was reliving those moments in the empty hallway outside the courtroom. She was feeling those rock-hard arms around her, the frantic heartbeat against her chest. She was remembering the look in those deep blue eyes....

All at once Brady knew why she hadn't wanted to talk about the incident, why she had felt so shaken. She realized that she had been allowed a rare glimpse deep inside a very guarded and private man. For those few moments Michael Snow had stood before her, naked and vulnerable, stripped to his soul. It seemed to her that to tell anyone else about it would be a kind of betrayal.

Judge Snow was human; Brady knew just how human he really was. For she knew with absolute certainty that in the depths of his soul Michael Snow was an angry, and even frightened, man.

Chapter 2

"Well," Kyle said, "I can see you're going to be a while—unless you're planning to have that bronzed?"

Brady said, "Hmm?"

"Your dinner. You are planning to eat it sometime today?"

"My dinner. Oh, yeah. Sorry. I guess I was—"

"Yeah, well, listen, I think I'm going to shove off. It's still raining, and I've got things to do."

"Okay," Brady murmured. "See you tomorrow."

"Monday."

"What?"

"You'll see me Monday. This is Friday."

"Oh. Oh, yeah, right. See you—"

"Actually you probably will see me tomorrow. Are you going to Sasha's party?"

"What?"

"Tomorrow night? Party at Sasha's? Naked orgies and mass acupuncture?"

"Oh. Yeah, I guess so."

"Right," Kyle said, and patted the top of her head. "Have a nice weekend."

Brady didn't see him go. She was lost in a maze of confusing thoughts, all having to do with Michael Snow. It wasn't unusual, really. She'd spent a great deal of time watching and sketching Judge Snow in his courtroom, and had always found him a fascinating man. But somehow this new awareness of the man inside the judge's robes had opened up a Pandora's box of questions, impressions and feelings that whirled around inside her like mischievous demons.

How old is he? Does he have a wife? Children? Where does he live? Does he like Aretha Franklin? Mexican food? Baseball?

She remembered that his fingers had felt warm against her face and that his breath had smelled of peppermint. She remembered that his eyes had been bloodshot and ringed with the purple smudges of exhaustion.

What's the matter with him? Why was he so angry? How can he possibly be *afraid*?

What's going on?

With a sigh of frustration, Brady stood up to leave. That was when she noticed the manila file folder on the floor under the judge's chair. Without a moment's thought or hesitation, she grabbed her purse, snatched up the folder and raced out of the cafeteria.

When she reached the elevators, the door of the farthest one was just closing. She called, "Your Honor—Judge Snow—" But if he was inside he gave no indication, and didn't stop. She had no choice but to punch the call button and wait impatiently for the next one.

As she rode to the ground floor, Brady knew that her heart was racing and her adrenaline pumping out of all proportion to the physical and emotional demands of what she was doing. She couldn't explain it—couldn't explain the excitement she felt or the sense of urgency—but as she burst out of the elevator and ran across the lobby, she felt as if the file she carried was a matter of life or death. Somehow she *had* to catch up with Judge Snow, *had* to return the file to him *tonight*.

There he was, just going down the courthouse steps, mindful of the treacherous footing, umbrella glistening in the light of the street lamps. Brady followed and was instantly soaked to the skin. She called, "Your Honor, please wait!" But in the noise of the rain and traffic, he couldn't hear her.

She gave a little grunt of frustration and hurled herself down the steps. The clip that held her hair in place came loose and skittered on ahead of her. She called again. "Judge Snow—wait! Please!"

This time he heard. At the edge of the curb, one hand on the doorhandle of a waiting taxicab, he turned to look back. Brady saw his face register alarm, then a question and finally recognition.

"Miss Brady," he said, his eyes coming to rest on the hair that had begun to drip rainwater into her eyes.

She hurriedly pulled it back from her face with her free hand and held out the folder with the other. "You left this upstairs. I thought it might be important."

"Ah. Yes. Thank you." The judge had already tilted his umbrella so that it sheltered them both. He added mildly, "Hardly worth getting yourself half drowned for, however."

His voice held a familiar trace of irony and dry amusement. Brady couldn't see him clearly—his face was in shadow and his form was only a tall silhouette—but it occurred to her all at once that Michael Snow seemed to be a very lonely man. A sense of loneliness and overwhelming isolation struck her like a physical force. She wanted to cry out in protest. No one, *no one* should be so alone!

Instead, she shivered.

"You're cold," the judge observed. "Don't you have an umbrella?"

Brady shrugged. "Oh, it's okay, my car's just..." She gestured vaguely toward the parking lot around the corner. "I'll...um. Well, good night." She turned away, but a hard hand captured her arm and drew her back under the shelter of the umbrella.

"Here, I'll walk you to your car." Ignoring Brady's inarticulate protest, the judge stooped to speak to the cab driver, then guided her firmly up the sidewalk toward First Street.

"Th-thanks, but you really don't have to d-do this." Brady's teeth were chattering, but from a strange nervous tension rather than the cold.

The judge didn't answer. They were standing on the edge of the curb, and he was looking over her head, studying the street. At this time of night, well after office hours and before the Friday-night Music Center crowd, it was nearly deserted—a wide, glistening emptiness stretching uphill toward the freeway. The hand on Brady's arm tightened.

She thought, Good heavens, I'm jaywalking with a judge! As she stepped off the curb she had a nervous impulse to giggle.

The judge's long legs easily spanned the rushing torrent in the gutter, but Brady had to jump over it. She stumbled, and he paused for a moment to steady her.

A block or so up the street, a car pulled away from the curb. Brady probably wouldn't have noticed it, except that it started to accelerate abruptly with a squealing of tires. In seconds it was careening down the wet street, out of control.

For the second time that day, Brady experienced the sensation of being encased in stone. But this time it was only for an instant, and then Michael Snow swore with a quiet vehemence that was more alarming than a scream. His fingers bit into the flesh of her upper arm, and in a voice that was hoarse with urgency he said, "Come on, *run!*"

He moved at a dead run across the slippery pavement, half carrying her. In that surrealistic nightmare of blackness and rain and noise, Brady looked up the street and felt her mouth form a wide, silent O of disbelief. The speeding car had changed course and was heading straight for them with the deadly intent of a guided missile.

She froze, mesmerized by flashing windshield wipers, by water droplets quivering on a broad hood, by a huge shiny chrome grille....

There was a loud roaring noise, a shout. Then she was moving, hurtling through the air, hitting the pavement and rolling over and over. She heard the squeal of abused tires, and suddenly she found herself facedown on the wet sidewalk with something large and heavy on top of her, pressing on her so that she couldn't breathe.

In the silent aftermath her first thought was, I'm alive! I must be alive, or I wouldn't need to breathe.

The weight on her back felt heavier. It was warm, but ominously still. She stirred a little as an experiment, and was profoundly relieved when a gust of expelled breath blew past her ear.

"Thank God," Judge Snow said. "Are you all right?"

"I will be," Brady answered, "if you'll just get off of me." Inexplicably the body on top of her began to shake with what felt like silent laughter.

Michael wasn't sure he *could* move. He was having a peculiar reaction to the sound of her voice, its brittle edge of annoyance reassuring him as nothing else could that she truly was alive and not seriously injured. It had been a close one, the closest yet, and even worse, it had almost taken out an innocent bystander. It was intolerable, but instead of the usual surge of rage, the trembling in the legs that came from an overabundance of adrenaline, he felt limp, absolutely drained. He wanted to lie still for a few moments and savor the sensations that proved he was alive—the asphalt smell of wet pavement, the pain of scrapes and bruises and the feel of a woman's body under his.

"Please," Brady said with some urgency. "I can't breathe."

"Sorry," Michael grunted. He rolled off her and sat up, bemused to discover that he still had his briefcase in his hand. He had no idea what had become of his umbrella.

The young woman heaved a sigh and rolled over onto her back. Michael thought, Incredible. I almost got her killed, and I don't even know her first name. On impulse he reached over and wiped raindrops from her face. When she opened her eyes and sat up slowly, he smiled ruefully down at her and said, "Crazy driver."

"Like hell! That guy was trying to kill us!" Her eyes were wide, and her voice crackled with outrage. Michael decided he admired her. She was sitting in the gutter in the pouring rain having just narrowly escaped death or grave injury, her teeth were chattering, she was wet and dirty and she had to be at the very least bruised. And she was *angry*.

He gazed at her in silence. She stared back at him and sat up. "He *was*," she said, her voice a little thinner, a little higher. "He was trying to kill us."

Michael got stiffly to his feet and held out his hand. "Come on."

"I'm not sure I can. My legs feel like—"

"I know the feeling," Michael said grimly. "But unless something's broken, I think you'd better give it a try. We can't stay here."

For a moment she looked as if she would say something, then thought better of it and wordlessly took his hand. He pulled her to her feet and then, to his utter astonishment, found himself holding on to her hard and tight. Her arms were around him, and his arms were around her, and for a few moments they just stood in the gutter like that, like lovers who know there will be no tomorrow. He felt her body tremble.

"Hey," he repeated after a moment, "we can't stay here."

"Because he might come back, you mean." Her voice sounded very small.

He took her arms and held her away from him. "Where's your car?"

She looked around as if she'd lost her bearings and said vaguely, "Um, over there."

"Give me your keys."

"They're in my purse."

It was lying on the sidewalk a few feet away. Michael picked it up and handed it to her. It was the size of a small suitcase, but it only took a moment for her to locate her car keys and hand them to him. He took the keys in one hand and her arm in the other. When she stumbled, it was very natural for him to slip his arm around her waist and let it remain there.

It was with approximately equal parts dismay and resignation that he discovered her car was a Jeep. Dismay because, although it did have a top, it wasn't exactly airtight, and they were both soaked and chilled to the skin. Resignation because, in a way he didn't fully understand yet, it seemed to suit her. Still, he hoped it wasn't far to her place. Even if he called a cab from there, it was beginning to look like a long time before he'd be stepping into a hot shower.

She didn't say a word when he handed her into the passenger seat and tossed his briefcase into the back. She just buckled her seat belt and sat there shivering while he walked around and slipped behind the wheel. When he had the heater going full blast he turned to her and said, "Where do you live?"

She cleared her throat. "Topanga Canyon."

"Oh, Lord."

She glanced at him and sniffed. "It's my father's place."

"Your father?"

"It's okay, he doesn't live there anymore. He died last year. I live alone."

"I'm sorry."

"That I live alone?"

Unreasonably annoyed, Michael snapped, "Don't be ridiculous," as he put the Jeep in gear and pulled jerkily out of the parking lot. It had been a while since he'd driven anything with four-wheel drive and a standard transmission. When they were on the freeway and heading west, he gave the woman beside him a brief glance and said, "I don't suppose you saw the license number."

She shook her head. "No."

"Description of the car?"

She considered that for a moment. "Late-model, dark. American, I think."

He nodded. "Pontiac. Pretty anonymous, actually." They were both silent, listening to the flapping of the Jeep's canvas doors, the thump of windshield wipers and the roar of wind and rain. Then Michael said gently, half to himself, "It could have been an accident, you know—slippery pavement, wet brakes."

"It wasn't." Her voice was flat, unequivocal.

Michael gave her another glance, this one of curiosity. "What makes you so positive?"

"Didn't you see the look on that guy's face? He didn't look scared, like you would if your car was out of control and you thought you were going to hit somebody. It was more like intent. Like he was in complete control and he *knew* he was going to hit somebody."

Michael's hands tightened on the steering wheel. Excitement zapped through him and settled in his belly with a hard, painful quivering. It took tremendous effort to keep his voice quiet and steady. "You say you *saw* him? Saw his face?"

He felt her turn her head to look at him. "Yes," she said, slowly but firmly. "I saw his face." And then, wonderingly: "I can draw him."

Michael whispered, "Good Lord." He didn't dare look at her; he had a feeling that he might be approaching some sort of calamitous breaking point, and behind the wheel of a car on a rainy freeway wasn't a good place for that to happen. After all the weeks of suspense and unrelieved tension, day after day of facing the possibility of his own death, was it possible that this young woman was about to do what neither he nor the police could? Could this girl with the Madonna smile and witch's eyes finally give his assassin a *face*?

In an anonymous hotel room high above the rain-slick streets of Los Angeles, the assassin stared into a mirror at a face that had never been recorded. Until today. The eyes were cold, intent. The brain behind them was just as cold, just as intent, thinking of the task at hand, of missed opportunities and of self-preservation. That girl—the artist. She had gotten in the way today. And she had become a very real and present danger. She would have to be dealt with.

There wasn't any easy way to get to Topanga Canyon from downtown L.A. Three freeways and a winding road that suffered mud and rock slides whenever it rained. Brady had never minded the drive before; it had seemed a small enough price to pay to live in a place where people kept goats, and where you could walk up a trail through thick oak mulch and come out on a knoll with an unspoiled view of the ocean. Tonight, though, it seemed like the back road to forever.

In spite of the fact that the Jeep's heater was blowing hot air in her face, she had never been so cold. Or so tired—a reaction of some kind, she supposed. She had a terrible desire to sleep, but she couldn't very well do that and just leave everything to Michael. It had been nice of him to take over the driving like that, when she had been so shaky, but he had to be at least as cold and wet and tired as she was, and besides, he'd just saved her life.

Michael. When had she begun thinking of him that way? He certainly wasn't any less a stranger to her than he'd been a couple of hours ago. She didn't have the faintest idea what to say to him. But on the other hand they'd barely escaped death together, and had hugged each other afterward, and after that she just couldn't seem to think of him as *Your Honor.*

Whatever her mind chose to call him, she was intensely conscious of him. He seemed very large, sitting there beside her in that small, enclosed space. He smelled of wet wool and other things that were less identifiable but very definitely masculine. Somehow he radiated warmth and comfort. Somehow he made her feel safe.

And yet, at the same time, she was very much aware of *his* needs, and of a strong and unfamiliar desire within herself to fill them. She knew that he was cold and wet, tired and shaken, but what was strange was that she wanted to make him warm and dry and happy. She wanted to comfort him, to make him laugh.

She'd never felt like that before, about anyone.

Shaking her head in bemusement, she drew his questioning glance, and when he asked what she was thinking about, she replied with the first thing that came into her head. "Nothing. I was just realizing that I didn't eat any dinner tonight. I guess I'm hungry."

"Then what were you doing in the cafeteria?" It was the voice she heard so often from the bench—dry, with a touch of irony.

"Oh, well, I sort of got sidetracked. I never got around to eating. Maybe we could find a McDonald's."

"McDonald's?"

"Or could you make that Taco Bell? I think there's one on the way."

"Taco Bell." His tone was still dry, but when he glanced at her Brady saw that he was smiling.

"This is nice," Michael said. He didn't know what he'd expected her place to be like; he had very little experience with women who dressed the way she did, drove Jeeps and ate at places called Taco Bell. But this room surprised him. It wasn't large, but it gave the impression of space, light and warmth, even with the darkness outside and rain pouring down the windows. And though it was as cluttered as he would have expected her living quarters to be, he found that he didn't mind that as much as he usually did. The clutter had a certain appeal, something indefinably homey that had to do with shabby but comfortable sofas, colorful afghans and an eclectic assortment of reading material.

She murmured "Thanks," and went to pull the drapes, shutting out the storm, closing them in with the sun-gold warmth of pine paneling and natural stone. "I'm sure glad the road was open." She threw him a smile over her shoulder as she knelt to turn on a gas log in the fireplace. "Sometimes when it rains we get mud slides. Sorry about the fire. We aren't allowed to have real wood fires—danger of sparks. You know, brushfires."

"Sounds to me like there might be more disadvantages to living out here than it's worth," Michael observed, moving closer to the fire. Closer to her. Her hair had fallen forward over one shoulder, and he found himself staring at the delicate shell of her exposed ear and wondering again what her first name was.

"There are a few," she admitted, standing up and brushing off her hands. "But I like it here." She was looking at him through a curtain of damp hair. There were unspoken questions in those pale blue eyes. He found them magnetic and unbelievably compelling.

"I'm sorry," he said, experiencing an unfamiliar awkwardness. "It seems a bit strange to have to ask under the circumstances, but could you please tell me your name?"

She gave him an odd look. "You know my name. Brady."

"I know, but I can hardly call you Miss Brady, can I? Or do you prefer Ms.?" He smiled ruefully. "After all we've been through together, I think we ought to be on a first-name basis. Mine is Michael."

She said, "I know. Mine's Brady."

Michael said, "Oh." He cleared his throat. "I'm sorry. Brady?"

"Flynn," she supplied, then shrugged and threw him a funny little smile. "That's okay. I thought it was kind of strange, you calling me by my first name. Sort of blew me away, you know? I mean, why would *you*, a judge..." Her voice faded into self-conscious laughter. Her gaze slid away. She clutched a handful of her hair and pulled it away from her face, and he saw that her cheeks were turning pink. With an odd little pang he also saw that there was a fresh abrasion on her forehead.

"Oh, God," she muttered suddenly, taking a deep breath. Her eyes slid away from his. "This is so strange. It doesn't seem real."

"I know." He reached out a hand and touched the scraped place on her face; he couldn't seem to help himself. When she flinched, he murmured, "Sorry," but instead of withdrawing his hand he let his fingers go where they wanted to go, toward her temple and into her hair. "I never meant for anyone else to get involved in this."

"This... it's happened before, hasn't it?"

He nodded. "Yes."

"Someone's trying to kill you. Someone tried to kill us."

"Yes," he said gently. "I'm sorry."

"Oh, God." She shut her eyes and drew in her breath. "It just doesn't seem real." She began to shake.

"I know," Michael said huskily, and pulled her into his arms. His fingers combed through her damp hair; his palm cradled her head against his shoulder. Her arms came around him. "I'm sorry. I wish—"

"Look, it's not your fault. It must be awful for you."

He laughed softly, not trusting himself to speak. He couldn't understand what was happening to him. He felt as if something was unraveling inside him.

Brady said, "You're shaking."

Again he managed a laugh. "Is that me? I thought it was you."

"I think it's both of us." He felt her arms move, tighten, felt her hands come up to touch his neck, his hair, his face. He took a deep breath and pressed his cheek against the top of her head, while his arms drew her closer, closer.

He thought, I don't even know this girl! What in heaven's name am I doing? But he didn't stop. It's comfort, just comfort, he told himself. It felt so good just to hold someone, to have someone hold him. It had been so damn long....

He felt her head move, felt her warm breath on his neck. He lowered his head and pressed his jaw against the side of her face. She turned her face slightly toward his.

He didn't mean to kiss her; he really didn't. That, he knew very well, was going beyond comfort. But her lips were so soft, so warm, and he just didn't want to stop. He couldn't understand what had happened to his self-control.

Without pulling away from her, he whispered, "I'm sorry."

"For what?"

"I didn't mean for this to happen."

"I know you didn't. But it's okay."

It wasn't, and he knew it. She was shaken, vulnerable. To take advantage of her now would be reprehensible. He had to stop this. But something in him cried out, Not yet, not yet!

Her mouth was there, soft, warm, incredibly sweet. He tasted it with his tongue, and she opened to him. It seemed such a *natural* thing.

He thought, This is crazy. And then, for a while, he didn't think at all. He only *felt*.

He felt her body all along the front of his. Not small and soft, the way he remembered Helen's, but firm and slender. And yet she fit so well. Her skin was soft; it felt like silk when he held her waist in his hands—and when in the world had *that* happened? Somehow his hands, craving more intimate contact, had slipped under the bottom of her sweater.

He felt her hands touching him. Like his, they had sought closer contact, creeping inside his coat and jacket so that he felt their warmth through his shirt as she stroked his back and sides with surprising gentleness. But most of all he felt her mouth, then lost himself in the sensations of tasting, caressing, exploring inside and out the full, firm texture of her lips, the warm, liquid softness inside, the unexpected vibrancy of her tongue. The way she responded to him, neither fighting nor urging, just *with* him, almost as if she knew exactly what he was feeling, what he wanted, what he *needed*.

He had to stop this—*now*.

He pulled away from her—probably one of the hardest things he'd ever done—but held on to her hands and stroked the inside of her wrists where tendons and veins lay just beneath the fragile skin. They both stared down at their hands and for a few moments said nothing.

Then Michael cleared his throat and said, "I think we'd better stop while we still can."

Brady's throat felt dry.

She whispered, "Do you want to?"

He shook his head. "No."

"Neither do I." Her heartbeat became thunderous. It came as a shock to hear herself say, "So why should we?"

Michael looked at her and saw her touch the hurt place on her lip with her fingers. It gave him a pang; he'd forgotten about it. He saw her throat move and felt a corresponding convulsion deep in his belly. For the life of him, he couldn't think of a reply.

The silence and tension seemed almost palpable. Brady felt a sense of unreality, as if there were a stranger in her body, saying things, doing things, she'd never done before. Surely she couldn't be saying, "If we both feel that way, what's wrong with it?"

Michael didn't know how to answer her. Half of him wanted to agree with her, but the other half just knew that it *was* wrong, if for no other reason than that it was wrong for *him*.

All of a sudden, as he looked down into her eyes, Michael felt a great gap opening between them, full of fundamental differences in values and viewpoints and philosophies. It wasn't something he could explain logically, but it made him feel lonely and a little sad and very, very tired.

He said, "I think we're both in need of a hot shower and some dry clothes." His voice was gravelly, but he didn't bother to clear it; he'd tried that already, and it hadn't done any good. "If you'll let me use your phone, I'll call a cab."

"You could take a shower here." Brady's voice seemed to echo inside her head. She felt cold now, as if she were coming out of a traumatic experience. "I could probably even find you some clothes, some of my dad's things."

Very gently Michael said, "I don't think that's such a good idea."

She made an odd little gesture, laying her hand lightly, fleetingly, against the front of his shirt. It was a movement that said so much. It said, I want you. I'm sorry. I understand. It's all right. And it said, Don't think for one minute that this is finished.

Michael said softly, more to convince himself than her, "You'll be all right, you know. You're perfectly safe. He—whoever he is—was after me, not you."

She just nodded. "The phone's over there. On the counter." She stood in front of the fireplace, rubbing her arms. He felt her eyes on him as he walked across the room to pick up the receiver.

Michael put it to his ear, listened for a few seconds, then set it carefully back in its cradle. He turned to look at her.

In a voice that sounded unfamiliar to him, he muttered, "The line's dead."

Chapter 3

There was a moment of tense silence. Brady watched Michael's face change subtly, watched it acquire the hard, wary look of a street fighter. It was a dangerous look, a look that, on anyone else's face, would have inspired fear in her.

But Brady knew what he was thinking and hurriedly managed a smile to reassure him. "Oh, yeah, that happens all the time during storms and things like that. They probably won't get it fixed until it stops raining. I'm sorry," she said. "It looks like you're stuck here after all."

She coughed and moved away from the fire, toward the kitchen and, obliquely, toward him. She didn't look at him. She knew that if she did, he would see in her face that she wasn't sorry at all that he was "stuck here." It wasn't that she felt afraid. In fact she felt detached, protected by a little cocoon of unreality from emotions too new and complex and frightening to cope with. But still, for reasons she didn't want to examine too closely, she didn't want him to go.

"Look, it really is okay if you stay. You can sleep in Dad's room; it even has its own bathroom. Small house, but two bathrooms. And I know I have an old bathrobe of his. You could put it on while your clothes are drying.''

''Brady,'' Michael said, smiling with that familiar irony, ''you can rest your case. I can see it's open-and-shut.'' He was rubbing the back of his neck as if it hurt him, and there were lines and hollows in his face she'd never seen before.

He's exhausted, she thought. The cocoon around her emotions cracked a little; she felt a tightness in her chest.

''Hey,'' she said breathlessly, ''why don't you let me take your coat? I'll hang it over a chair by the fire. Come on, your jacket, too. That's right.'' She helped him take it off, but was careful not to touch *him*, especially his hands. Her own were shaking, and for reasons she couldn't quite figure out she didn't want him to know.

''This is, *was*, Dad's room.'' Brady opened the door and turned on the light, trying not to look at the room that still held so much of Sean Flynn—overflowing bookcases, drawings hanging on the paneled walls, framed and unframed—scenes of famous trials, infamous faces, dramatic moments, sketches of Brady as a baby, a child, a teenager. ''That's the bathroom over there, closet there. Feel free to help yourself to anything you need. You're taller than Dad, but I guess a bathrobe wouldn't...'' Her voice trailed away. Michael was walking slowly around the room gazing intently at the pictures on the walls. He threw her a quizzical look, and she shrugged, trying to laugh. ''Some parents are camera freaks; my dad used a pad and pencil.''

''Quite an interesting mix of subjects,'' Michael commented dryly. ''Sirhan Sirhan, the Manson family, and—?'' He tapped a large framed pastel and lifted one eyebrow.

Brady coughed and muttered, ''That's me—senior prom.'' And then, to her complete surprise, she added, ''I wasn't a lovely child.''

He gave her a long look, one she couldn't read. ''Your dad evidently disagreed.''

She gave an embarrassed laugh, and that surprised her, too. She'd grown up amidst love and security, in spite of having no mother, and she couldn't remember ever feeling self-conscious before. "Well, you know how dads are."

His face closed almost imperceptibly. "No, I can't say that I do. I'll have to take your word for it."

Well, I guess that answers one question, Brady thought. She coughed again and muttered, "Well. I'll have to get you some towels." She stepped through the door and closed it carefully behind her, then leaned against it, quivering with tight inner tremors like a plucked bowstring.

She thought, I'm exhausted, too. I must be.

Either that or the burrito and two tacos she'd eaten in the car on the way home weren't sitting well on top of all the excitement. Why else would she have such a terrible case of butterflies?

She found a clean beach towel with the logo of the 1984 Olympic Games on it, several hand towels and washcloths in assorted colors and a bath mat printed to look like a can of Budweiser. When she knocked on Sean's bedroom door there was no answer, so she went in. The room was empty, and the bathroom door was closed. She put the towels on the foot of the bed and went out again, tiptoeing.

In her own bathroom she kicked off her boots and turned on the hot water, and while the room filled up with steam she peeled off all her clothes and left them in a dismal pile in the middle of the floor. She discovered bruises—a series of small ones on her upper arms where Michael's fingers had dug into her flesh with desperate purpose, bigger ones on her hip and thigh from when she hit the pavement. Funny, she hadn't felt anything at the time. Shock could be a blessed protection, she thought. It insulated the mind from things it couldn't handle: pain too terrible to bear, experiences too awful to contemplate, reality too incredible to believe.

But shock wears off eventually. As she stood in the shower, letting hot water sluice over her face and body, Brady wondered when it was going to hit her that tonight someone had almost killed her. On purpose. It hadn't hit her yet, because no matter how many times she said that to herself, it still seemed like the plot of a TV cop show. Or a movie, with Charles Bronson or Clint Eastwood playing the lead.

What seemed every bit as incredible to Brady as the fact that someone had tried to kill her was the fact that the Honorable Michael A. Snow—George Washington incarnate—was at this very moment standing under a stream of hot water approximately eighteen inches away from her. In the interests of economy, the two bathrooms had been built back-to-back, incorporating all the plumbing for both into one wall. It occurred to Brady that if she had X-ray vision as she stood facing the shower head she would be staring directly at Judge Snow's naked chest.

It was a deliciously wicked thought. Brady held on to it with giddy desperation in order to keep her mind from carrying the image a step further, beyond fantasy and into recent memory. Much better to keep to fantasy, like a Doris Day movie.

Television, movies, a judge in her bathroom, speeding cars trying to run her down—just fantasy, nothing more. Fantasy was simple, neat and tidy—the good guys always beat the bad guys; the hero and heroine always fell in love and lived happily ever after.

Reality, on the other hand, was complex and frightening, awkward and painful, and the outcome was never certain.

Brady came out of her bedroom wearing an old pair of UCLA sweats and a towel turban just as Michael Snow was coming out of Sean's bedroom next door. He was wearing sweats, too, an old pair of Sean's. They hit him just above the ankles. His feet were bare.

Brady stopped so abruptly that her turban unwound and tumbled to her shoulders. In a daze, she reached up with both hands to comb her wet hair with her fingers.

She heard Michael say in a wondering voice, "So that *is* the way you do it."

She murmured absently, "Do what?" She was staring at his bare feet. There was something defenseless about those feet; something touchingly human. At the sight of them something happened to her defenses. Suddenly, like the towel turban, her protective cocoon unwound, leaving her emotions exposed and vulnerable.

Her eyes began a slow, wondering journey upward.

"I thought these would be more practical than a bath-robe. I hope it was all right."

"What?" Brady's gaze had reached the mouth she had studied so intently and drawn so often. It struck her that now she not only knew what it looked like when he smiled, she knew what it felt like, tasted like. Memory assaulted her; her senses reeled. She felt it all again. It *had* been real—his hands caressing her, his mouth discovering hers, tracing the cut place so gently it hadn't even hurt her.

In near-panic she jerked her eyes upward once more and found his eyes. They were shadowed, the expression in them intent but unreadable. The desire to touch him, to be in his arms again, to feel his hands and his mouth again, was so overwhelming that it was almost a physical pain. But her awareness of his isolation from her was just as strong. For reasons she couldn't begin to understand, he had put can-yons between them a mile wide, built walls so thick she couldn't even try to break through them. He was George Washington at his most austere; she might as well contem-plate kissing Mount Rushmore.

She thought, It's as if he's trying to deny it ever hap-pened.

But Brady knew it *had* happened. She had held Michael Snow in her arms and felt the urgency in him—a desperate need that she realized had held more longing than passion. And though she knew it wasn't what he'd intended, in those few moments he had managed to create a need in *her*. Now it was *she* who felt the longing. And what scared her was the possibility that it was a need only he could fill.

"Oh," she said, jerking her eyes away from his, back to the broad expanse of his chest. "Sure it's okay. I said it was, didn't I?" It was Sean's Notre Dame sweatshirt—a favorite of his. It hung a bit differently on Michael's lean frame. Brady turned away abruptly. Suddenly she felt as though she needed to put some distance between them herself, as if she didn't quite have enough air to breathe. "Hey, are you hungry? Can I get you anything?"

"It's all right; I've eaten, remember?" His voice was gentle.

"Yeah, but that was quite a while ago. Look, you're going to be here a while. If you're going to be polite, you'll starve to death."

"All right, all right," Michael said, laughing. "Now that you mention it, I'd love some coffee—if you have it. Don't go to any trouble."

From the safe distance of the kitchen doorway she turned to look at him. "Sorry, I don't have any coffee. Don't you know coffee's bad for you?"

"Really?" He was looking bemused. "How about some hot cocoa?"

"Chocolate's bad for you, too, but I've got some Postum."

"Postum," Michael murmured faintly. "What on earth is that?"

"I don't know, actually. I think it's made out of grain. Anyway, it doesn't ruin your stomach or keep you awake. You could try it; I think it's pretty good. Or I've got some herb tea."

"I think I'll try the Postum," Michael said, covering a yawn with a chuckle. "Need any help?"

"Oh, no. Thanks anyway. Just make yourself comfortable. It'll just take a minute."

It was a relief to be busy and alone in the familiar kitchen, away from all the strange undercurrents and tensions evoked by Michael's presence. The air seemed cooler, quieter. Brady took several deep breaths and combed her hair back with her fingers. She took extra time locating two Los Angeles Dodgers coffee mugs that matched, then set a tray with napkins and spoons and a little dish with sugar and another one with non-dairy creamer. When the water was hot she spooned dark brown crystalline powder into the mugs and poured the water in, then stirred until everything was thoroughly dissolved. At last she took another deep breath and carried the tray out to the living room. She set it carefully on the coffee table, then straightened and stood gazing down at the Honorable Michael Snow.

He was sound asleep, half sitting, half reclining, in one corner of the sofa, his head pillowed on his arm.

Brady stood there for a long time looking at the judge's sleeping face. She saw the dark crescents of his lashes and the faintest tracing of veins across his eyelids. She saw the shadow of a day's growth of beard and the lock of hair that had fallen across his forehead like a comma. She was thinking that he bore no resemblance at all to Mount Rushmore. And she was thinking that life was really surprising sometimes, and very, very precious.

After a while she went into her father's bedroom and took the comforter off the bed. She carried it out to the living room and spread it over Michael, taking special care to tuck it around his bare feet. After another moment's consideration she went back to the bedroom for a pillow. When she tried to slip it under his head, he stirred and murmured, "Thanks," but didn't wake up.

Brady went to the bathroom and brushed her teeth. Then she turned off all the lights except the one over the sink in Sean's bathroom. After some thought she left the gas log on, turned down low. She stood in her bedroom for a few minutes, hugging herself in the darkness and listening to the rushing sound of the rain. Then she picked up the afghan that lay across the foot of the bed and went out to the living room again. Michael had moved a little, settling more comfortably into his corner. Brady wrapped the afghan around herself and curled up in the opposite corner with her feet tucked under her, wriggling down until her head rested on the arm of the couch.

Outside, the cold wet blackness pressed against the windows, but inside the house the darkness was like gray velvet, enveloping and warm. The noises of the rain and the fire and Michael's breathing created a soothing, gentle monotony.

Then the darkness hardened to brittle intensity, like obsidian; it reflected light in distorted patterns, like a funhouse mirror. She heard a rushing sound that grew louder, then louder yet, until it became a roar that filled her head— and still it grew louder. She put her hands over her ears, but she couldn't shut out the noise. The patterns of light acquired form, then density and mass—steel and chrome and glass, and behind the glass a face, cold and intent. A missile—no, a monster—and she was its target, its quarry. She knew it, but she couldn't make herself move, couldn't get out of the way. She stood paralyzed while the thing hurled itself down upon her....

Hard hands gripped her arms. She felt herself being lifted, thrown bodily through the air. She braced herself for the impact, but instead felt herself being enveloped in warmth and softness. The roaring receded, becoming only a distant whisper of sound. And then she heard a voice murmuring words of comfort, meaningless fragments of sentences, the sounds a child hears waking from a nightmare in loving arms.

Nightmare. Of course. It was only a nightmare. She made a sound, a little sobbing laugh of relief, and heard an approving chuckle in response. "Yes," the voice crooned, "it's all right now. Go back to sleep."

"Hold me," Brady said.

"I will. Go to sleep now. You're safe here."

Michael shifted her weight, trying to find a more comfortable position for both of them. She gave a sigh and cuddled against him, aligning her body with his so naturally that it felt like something she'd been doing for years. Her hair tickled his nose; he flattened it with his hand and tucked her head into the curve of his neck and shoulder. He felt the moist heat of her breath on his skin and timed his own breathing to match hers.

You're safe here.

A gust of wind blew a flurry of raindrops against the window. Michael turned his head slightly to look at the shiny glass and the darkness beyond. He took a deep breath that lifted the head nestled just under his chin, then closed his eyes.

No one on earth outside this room knew where he was. As long as the rain poured down and the phone stayed dead, he was stuck here, isolated from the world. No one could have followed him. It was Friday. Until Monday morning, or whenever he chose to surface, not a soul except the woman sleeping in his arms would know where he was. For the first time in too many exhausting, nerve-racking weeks, Michael felt safe.

In the dark hotel room the assassin was awake, too, staring out the window at the rain and pacing in restless fury. The quarry had escaped, gone to earth. There was nothing to be done now but wait for them to surface. Sooner or later they would have to, and when they did... The assassin smiled. It was just a matter of time and patience.

Brady woke again when the night was thinning into dawn. She lay still, listening, feeling that particular ambiguity that characterizes the attitude most native Angelenos have toward rain. In Southern California the rains come seldom. When they do, sometimes it seems that they try to atone for the months of neglect, and their blessings arrive spiked with disaster. Soil unaccustomed to moisture takes on liquid form; houses slide down mountainsides, and mountainsides slide into houses. Dry riverbeds become torrents, and another foot or two of California tumbles into the Pacific Ocean. When a storm lasts longer than a few hours, Angelenos feel vague, primitive stirrings of unease.

But Brady heard another sound, a sound with a firm and reassuring rhythm. She concentrated on that sound, and it expanded in her ears until it blocked out the noise of the rain. She stirred and snuggled closer to its source. Her hand went searching for it, burrowing through layers of blanket and clothing until she found warm skin, silky hair and firm muscle. Beneath her palm the sound became something she felt rather than heard, a source of strength and comfort. The vague fears receded, and she slept.

Michael woke up with the feeling that something was missing. He felt lighter, as though something he'd been carrying around with him for a long time had disappeared. He also felt disoriented at first. He jerked his head off the pillow and looked around, then down at himself, stretched full length on a couch, covered haphazardly with a quilt and an afghan. Brady's couch. He'd fallen asleep, and she'd covered him with the quilt, and later...

Brady. What a strange sort of woman she was. Well, perhaps it wasn't so much that she was strange as that it was strange that he, Michael Snow, was here with her. Twenty-four hours ago he'd barely known her name, and now here he was, wearing a pair of her late father's sweats, having just spent the night with her in his arms! She was gone now, but he remembered it all, remembered feeling her body's warmth all along his, her head a tender weight on his chest.

For one bemused moment he wondered if that was what he thought he was missing. He sat up and stretched his stiff body experimentally, but though he was aware of all his sore places, he experienced such a surge of joy and exhilaration that he realized suddenly what really was missing. It was the feeling of impending doom he'd been carrying around for so long. For the first time in weeks, in spite of the fact that he was in the house of a stranger, he felt that he could truly relax. *No one* knew where he was.

He turned and looked across the room to the telephone on the tile counter between the kitchen and living room, and felt the slightest twinge of guilt. It was morning; someone must have reported the phones being out by this time, and linemen were on call twenty-four hours a day. He knew he ought to check and see if it was working. Very probably it was. He told himself he ought to at least try to call a cab.

At that moment Brady came in from the kitchen carrying a tray. She was wearing jeans and a red sweater with a purple teddy bear on it. She'd tied her hair up in a ponytail with a piece of purple chiffon. The ends of the chiffon were playing peekaboo with the brown-gold strands of hair that cascaded over her neck and ears. Michael was gazing at her hair in silent awe when she said, "Morning. I went ahead and warmed up the Postum in the microwave. Are you hungry? I've got cereal and milk—the milk is goat's milk; I hope that's okay. This lady up the hill gives me milk and eggs—" She stopped, sounding out of breath.

"What kind of cereal?" Funny, her breathlessness was making him feel the same way.

"Captain Crunch."

"Captain *what*?" She at least had the grace to look sheepish. Michael shook his head and grinned. "This from the person who tells me coffee's bad for me. Listen," he said, standing up and indulging in a monstrous stretch, "I tell you what. You come show me where things are, and I'll make us some breakfast."

She was staring at his chest; for some reason she seemed slightly stunned. "Uh" she said, then shook herself and croaked, "You can cook?"

He gave her his most dignified look. "What's the matter? Can't a man know how to cook? I thought you were a member of the liberated generation."

"Well, yeah." She tilted her head to one side and regarded him quizzically. "It's just that I never thought of you—I mean, it's hard to imagine—well, geez, you're a *judge*."

Michael laughed. It felt good to laugh. "What do you think a judge is—God?" She opened her mouth, closed it again, then shrugged, looking slightly guilty. The look on her face made him wonder just what she had been thinking about him. He reflected that it sometimes gives a person pause to catch a glimpse of his image through a stranger's eyes. "Hey," he said, putting on a look of extreme modesty, "even judges have to eat."

"Eating is one thing," she pronouced gravely. "Cooking is something else. You have to *learn* to cook."

"I wasn't born a judge," Michael said dryly. "At various times in my life I've been a lot of things that have required skills other than sitting around in a robe making decisions. That basically is what I do, you know—make decisions. I'm not God." He recognized the arrogance in the disclaimer and despised himself for it. He didn't know why he felt defensive, or why the weight of his professional image should suddenly seem onerous when it never had before. He just knew that she was making him feel like some bearded Solomon, and that wasn't what he wanted. Not today. Today he wanted to feel young, carefree. Today he wanted to forget that somewhere out there an assassin was waiting. Today he was safe. Today he wanted to be happy.

"Come on, lead me to your refrigerator. Where there's milk and eggs, there's hope!" Michael reached out to tweak a strand of her hair. Her eyes flew to his, and she caught her lower lip with the tips of her even white teeth. She turned away abruptly, and his hand fell to the back of her neck.

Her neck—how warm it was, how vital, and yet how fragile. How well it fit the curve of his hand. If he lifted his hand just a little, he could cradle the back of her head in his palm; with the lightest pressure he could turn her head and tilt it upward. She would respond to his unspoken request—he knew that beyond any shadow of doubt. She would turn to him, and her mouth would be soft, warm and sweet.

Michael swore silently. He wasn't free, could never be free, not of things like conscience and responsibility. For a few seconds longer he clung to the vision, fighting the temptation of his imagination. What was wrong with him? Here he was, stormbound with a beautiful woman—a beautiful, *willing* woman. There was no reason in the world why he shouldn't do what his body was telling him to do. And yet . . .

He let his hand drop away from her neck, listening with deep regret to the soft sigh of her expelled breath.

Chapter 4

Brady was sitting on a stool with her elbows on her drawn-up knees and her chin in her hands, watching Michael mix eggs and milk together with a fork. She was having to rearrange quite a few of her thoughts and preconceptions, both about him and about herself.

It was becoming very clear to her that Michael Snow wasn't entirely what he'd appeared to be. It wasn't so much that he was different as that he was a great deal *more*. The man who had become so familiar a figure to her in his judge's robes, the man she'd captured in dozens of drawings—that man had seemed all-powerful, austere and self-assured. A monument almost bigger than life, godlike and unapproachable. But in the last twenty-four hours she'd discovered so many other things about him—things she'd somehow missed in her preoccupation with line and form and likeness. Things like the anger that smoldered behind his dark blue eyes or the restraint that rippled through his body, hinting at other unsuspected depths and passions.

Things like his hands. In all the times she'd drawn the man, why hadn't she ever noticed his hands? They were square and strong, like his jaw, but there was grace in their movements and sensitivity in their touch. Just now he pushed up the sleeves of the sweatshirt, and Brady watched the muscles in his forearms flex and bunch. She found herself rubbing absently at the marks his strong fingers had left on her arms. A powerful man, Michael Snow, in more ways than one, but a man who knew when to use his power and when to keep it leashed.

Dad would have liked him. The thought came to Brady unexpectedly, making her smile. A good lad, Sean would have said; a good man to have at your back when the fightin' starts.

Because she was accustomed to thinking in terms of the graphic arts, it occurred to her that what was happening to her perceptions was like a scene in a movie, when a drawing gradually becomes the opening scene. One minute the viewer sees a painting or a line drawing, and then the picture takes on color, texture, depth, movement, sound, *life*. The scene becomes real, compelling, and suddenly the audience is intrigued by its mysteries, involved in the story.

"What's wrong?"

Brady blinked, bringing Michael's face into focus. There was a wry quirk to his mouth, a quizzical light in his eyes. She cleared her throat and said, "Wrong?"

"Yeah. You were sitting there scowling at me."

"Was I? Sorry, I guess I was just thinking."

"Thinking hard, by the looks of it. What about?"

"Oh," Brady hedged, and then said in exasperation, "well, you, of course."

"Oh, yeah?" Michael raised his eyebrows at her, then reached for the pepper shaker and said blandly, "What about me?"

What, indeed. And what, Brady wondered, about *me*? That was the real question. Michael Snow was precipitating a minor identity crisis inside her. In response to him, she was thinking unfamiliar thoughts, feeling unfamiliar feelings, behaving in unfamiliar ways. She'd always been fascinated with people, but as objects to be drawn with her pencils and paper. Lines and shadings, shapes of features, bone structure, facial expressions. She'd had very little time to spend thinking about the emotion behind the expression, the person inside the bone structure, until Michael. For some reason Michael seemed to have awakened in her a vast, insatiable curiosity. She wanted to know everything there was to know about him—his past and his present, his likes and dislikes, what he thought about things, how he felt.

But she couldn't very well ask him all that, so she had to be satisfied with one small question. "I was just wondering where you learned to cook."

Michael snorted. "There's nothing very complicated about making an omelet."

Frustrated by his evasiveness, Brady said carefully, "It isn't what you're making, it's the way you're doing it." At his interrogative look she straightened her back and said firmly, "With assurance."

But, she thought, you do everything with assurance. *Everything*. A flood of sensual memories inundated her.

"Well," Michael said, "I guess I have had quite a bit of experience." He was intent on his task and oblivious to her, thank goodness, or he would surely have seen what was written so plainly on her face.

Brady covered her hot cheeks with her hands and murmured, "Experience?"

"When you're single," she heard him say quietly, "you can either eat out a lot or learn to feed yourself. Or, more probably, both."

Brady lowered her hands and stared at him. "You're not married?"

"No." He threw her a glance. "Divorced." And then, dryly, he added, "You seem surprised."

"I guess I am."

"Why?" His smile was sardonic. "Is that something else you can't picture a judge doing?"

"No. It's just that after last night—" She stopped, suddenly embarrassed. But she clearly wasn't going to get any help from him, so she made a helpless gesture with her hands and blurted, "I just assumed that was the reason for last night. The reason you didn't...."

He didn't answer immediately. She watched his hands as he carefully covered the omelet pan, took it off the burner and turned off the gas. She saw his shoulders move as he took a breath and let it out. Finally he said, "No," and shook his head. "That wasn't the reason for last night." He turned to face her. His eyes were dark and thoughtful and very direct.

Brady thought, This court is now in session.

Michael said, "I'm not sure I can explain."

"You don't have to," Brady said, hunching her shoulders and gazing steadily at the omelet pan.

"Yes," Michael said softly. "I think I do." But he wasn't sure he could. He felt the same way he had last night, as if they'd been brought together by a time warp, as if they were from two different worlds. "Last night was..." He took a deep breath and began again. "It was a matter of timing. You were—we were both upset, scared, vulnerable. What happened was understandable under those circumstances. But to give in to the moment would have been irresponsible. Don't you agree?"

She nodded; what else could she do? But she went on gazing at him, her head tilted at a slight angle, and there was something in her eyes that made him feel a little bit fraudulent.

So he went on trying to explain, hoping that by making things absolutely clear to her he might find a better way to define his feelings in his own mind. "Listen, what happened shook us both up pretty badly. But where I was at least somewhat prepared, even expecting—"

"Expecting? *The note!*" Brady interrupted suddenly. "That's what that was all about, wasn't it? Yesterday, when I ran into you."

"Yes." Michael gazed at her with mixed feelings, not sure whether he was relieved or disappointed that they'd left one difficult subject for another. He was wondering how little he could get away with telling her, and regretting the need to tell her anything at all. If only he hadn't forgotten that file. What in God's name had possessed her to tear after him like that, anyway? If only she'd left the silly thing lying on the cafeteria floor, she wouldn't be here now, in the middle of his nightmare.

"What—" Brady said, then stopped to clear her throat. In a very low voice she asked, "What's going on?"

"Oh..." Michael made a throwaway gesture with his hand. "I've received some death threats. It's not that unusual, really." He gave her a lopsided smile. "One of the perks of my job, I suppose. But this guy seems to mean business."

"Who...?"

"If we knew that, we'd be able to put a stop to him, wouldn't we?"

"We?"

"The police."

"Oh."

"We're proceeding on the assumption that the threats are connected with one of my cases, the most likely being the current one, of course." He knew that he sounded pedantic, almost as if he was summarizing for a jury. It just seemed easier that way, as if this was just another case, one that concerned someone else. "This kind of tactic—intimidation, strong-arm stuff—has been typical of the Gianelli family's activities in Detroit and New Orleans. And there have been, shall we say, certain characteristics that seem to point to a professional contract. The only thing is . . ."

He paused, frowning, and Brady whispered, "Professional contract?"

Michael glanced at her. "Yeah. Except that we aren't so sure about that now."

Her voice was very faint. "Why not?"

"Because," he said matter-of-factly, turning to lift the omelet pan from the stove, "last night was the third try. If it had been a professional job—" he took the lid off of the pan "—it would have succeeded long before now."

In silence they watched the omelet slowly deflate.

"I'm sorry," Michael said at last.

Brady looked up in surprise. "What for?"

He deftly cut the omelet in two with the pancake turner and slid half onto her plate. "This isn't your affair," he said distantly. "I'm sorry you had to get involved."

She gave him a long look. "I'm a big girl, Judge Snow." For a few pulse beats longer her eyes held his; then she turned, picked up her fork and stabbed it into her omelet.

Michael set the pan in the sink, straddled the stool next to hers and picked up his own fork. They ate in a curiously tense, uncomfortable silence, listening to the rain spattering fitfully against the kitchen window. Beyond the watery glass Michael could see a patch of brown hillside and the gnarled gray branches of live oak trees.

A cold, wet, miserable morning. He'd give a lot for a cup of honest-to-goodness coffee.

What in the world was he doing here, anyway? He really ought to try again to call a cab.

"So," Brady said after a while, "what are you doing about it?"

Michael turned his head to look at her. She was poking fitfully at her breakfast with her fork. There was a pugnacious set to her mouth and chin that reminded him of the woman who had stood bruised and shaken in the gutter last night, breathing fire and fury. Brady Flynn. She had an Irish temper, all right, and he had a suspicion that she also possessed the Irishman's love of a good fight.

As he stared at that stony profile, so completely at odds with the cascade of undisciplined hair and the ridiculous purple bow, he realized that he'd been thinking of her all along as being very young. It came to him suddenly and with an odd sense of shock that she was a grown woman. *I'm a big girl, Judge Snow.*

The thought shook him so badly that he reached for his coffee mug and downed several swallows of its contents before he realized what he was drinking. The crazy thing was, the stuff didn't taste half bad.

"Doing?" he asked, frowning.

"Uh-huh." She turned a level gaze on him. "I assume you aren't just walking around L.A. waiting for somebody to take potshots at you. What were the other two tries, by the way?"

Michael smiled thinly. "Potshots. The first one shattered the reading lamp in my study one Sunday evening. That was when I took the police's advice and moved into a high-rise apartment building." He couldn't keep the bitter twist from his lips. "All sorts of security—it's like living in a prison cell. Let's see, the second one got the windshield of my car as I was waiting at a traffic light. The police have my car now, and I take cabs for security's sake. Less possibility of getting blown to kingdom come when I turn on the ignition."

"What are the police doing? Don't you have a body-guard or something?"

"I've refused police protection."

"For God's sake, why?"

Michael had to swallow a surge of anger before he could answer her. He focused a hard stare on the rain-washed windows and said coldly, "As a compromise I've agreed to certain alterations in my life-style, a few of which I've already mentioned. This person has cost me my home, my car and a great deal of my personal freedom. I refuse to allow him to take away my privacy, as well.''

''I see.'' A little frown hovered around her eyes. ''How come I never heard about any of this? How come it hasn't been—''

''In the papers?'' Michael snorted and got up to put his dishes in the sink. ''Because that's the way I wanted it.''

''Oh, right, your privacy. Is that why you're such a mediaphobe?''

''A *what*?''

''That's what my friend Kyle calls you. It means you don't like reporters—cameramen, TV, newspapers, any of it.''

''Oh, I don't think that's true,'' Michael said mildly. He turned to face her and leaned back against the counter with his arms folded across his chest. His eyelids dropped, and his voice became a lazy purr. ''I feel that the dissemination of information to the public is necessary. What I don't like is the arrogance of the media, the idea that the right of the public to information takes precedence over the individual's rights to privacy, life, liberty, pursuit of happiness, fair trial—''

''Your opinion shows bias, Your Honor.'' Her tone was light, but Michael didn't miss the spark of anger behind her cool blue eyes. He carefully kept his own voice dry and placid—his bench voice.

''On the contrary, it's a judgment based on a body of evidence. Personal experience, documented cases—''

''And so you condemn all of us?''

''Far from it. For example, I find your friend Kyle's television news spots to be extremely well researched and responsible. And your work is both accurate and perceptive.''

''Thank you,'' Brady said stiffly. ''I suppose I should be grateful to you. If it wasn't for your ban on cameras, I wouldn't have a job. Though I bet if you had your way you'd ban me, too.''

"Miss Flynn," Michael said very softly, "if I wanted to ban the press from my courtroom, let me assure you, I could."

She gazed at him in silence. He saw her swallow and instantly felt ashamed. She was no match for him in a war of words, and he'd gone after her with heavy artillery. He'd treated her like an adversary, when all she'd done was open her home to him. His sense of regret was so profound that he couldn't even bring himself to apologize.

Brady was feeling more than regret. What she felt was painful and sharp, an anguished sense of loss, the feeling that she'd had something of tremendous value in her grasp and that now it was slipping away.

She'd come to see Michael Snow as a man in a shell, a man so afraid of exposing his vulnerabilities that he'd encased himself in armor. Under the bludgeonings of circumstance, the armor had cracked in spots, allowing her, for a few brief hours, to see inside. He'd even reached out and touched her, but now the cracks were closing up again, leaving her feeling strangely bereft. She had a sudden urge to touch him physically, to reassure herself that the warm body and comforting arms that had held her last night while she slept had indeed belonged to him.

"Well," she said lightly, hopping off her stool, "I guess I'd better be grateful you like my work, then."

"Brady," Michael said with gravel in his voice, and then, softly, "I want you to know how much I appreciate everything."

"No problem. Hey, thanks for breakfast. It was really good."

His smile was slightly sardonic. "No problem. Well—listen, that phone's probably in working order by now. I suppose I really ought to call a cab and get out of your hair, let you get on with whatever you do on Saturdays."

"I don't do much, actually," Brady said. "Laundry, shopping, stuff like that."

"Doesn't sound like much fun."

"Sometimes I go for a hike—you know, through the state park. There's a place I like to go, a place where you can see the ocean."

"I don't know." He looked doubtfully out the window. "Doesn't seem like a very good day for it. Any other options?"

"Well," said Brady, "I'll probably read."

"Uh-huh. Well, then, I'd better get on my way." He took a deep breath and reached past her to put his hand on the receiver. Brady saw him move his shoulders as if shifting a weight.

Before she realized what was happening, her hand shot out to cover his. She heard herself say breathlessly, *"Wait!"*

At his questioning glance, she found that her heart was racing madly. She opened her mouth, closed it again, then finally said, "You can't go yet."

With real curiosity, he asked, "Why not?"

"Because..." Because, Brady thought with an unexpected wave of loneliness, I don't want you to. Because it's Saturday, and it's raining, and I'm alone with nothing in particular to do, and I want you to stay and do nothing in particular with me. Because, she thought, this time in surprise, I like you, Michael A. Snow. And I like being with you.

Suddenly, something occurred to Brady, something that, with all that had happened since last night, they'd both forgotten.

"Because," she said triumphantly, "I said I could draw the man in the car. Don't you remember?"

"Yes." He stared down at her hand. When she moved it, he slowly pulled his away from the telephone. "Yes, I remember. Brady, look, are you sure? It was dark. It was raining. It happened so fast."

She tapped the outer corner of her eye, automatically using the gesture she always used with Kyle. "I have a camera in here—that's what Dad always said. I only need a split second. How do you think I get all those courtroom action scenes?"

Michael murmured, "It is a unique talent." There was respect in his eyes. At his prolonged look, Brady felt herself grow warm with pride.

"Well," she said, clearing her throat, "I'll get my sketchbook. It's in my purse."

"Will it make you nervous if I watch you?" Michael asked when she came back to the counter with her tablet and pencil box.

"Oh, no, not at all." But as she settled herself on her stool she flipped quickly to a clean page, carefully folding the filled pages out of sight. For reasons she didn't entirely understand, she found that she didn't want him to know that at least half the drawings in the book were of him.

And despite her disclaimer she did feel a little nervous having him there at her back, almost but not quite touching her. To distract herself from the strange inner quivering his nearness was causing, she said conversationally, "You know, I've actually seen that face more than once." At his start of surprise she glanced up and gave him a tight little smile. "I saw it quite a few times last night . . . in my nightmares."

"Ah, yes. The nightmares. Was that what they were all about?" His voice was low, husky.

She looked back at the image that was taking shape on the white page and nodded. For a moment it was all there again, the feeling of cold, and of being turned to stone, the acid taste of terror. She shuddered, and felt Michael's hand touch the back of her neck.

"I thought so," he said. "I'm sorry." He stroked her briefly, then gave her neck a gentle squeeze and let his hand fall away.

Brady suddenly had an overwhelming urge to swallow, but when she did, her throat felt tight and achy. For a while she drew with dogged concentration, then gave the tablet a little push and murmured, "There, I think that's it."

They both stood staring down at the face on the tablet. In the silence the rain pushed against the windows—almost, Brady thought, as if it had a purpose. As if it was a wild thing, trying to get in....

The face of the assassin. A gaunt face, faintly exotic-looking, eyes dark and intent, mouth and chin set in lines of deadly determination. Just a face, undecorated by hairstyle or clothing; those things had been in shadow. The face was completely anonymous, and yet ...

Brady found that she was rubbing absently at her arms and, looking down, discovered that they were covered with goose bumps. She shuddered, and Michael said quietly, "Brady, what's wrong?"

She looked at him and tried to smile. "This is really weird." She tried to laugh, but her eyes were pulled back to the drawing as if by a magnet, and the laugh died in her throat. She whispered, "So weird."

"Brady, what is it? Something about that face?"

"You're not going to believe this," she said slowly. "I don't know where, or when, but I know I've seen this face before."

Chapter 5

Michael said, "Are you sure?" It was an automatic response; Brady knew he didn't doubt her.

She nodded. "Yes, but it's out of context. Like when you run into your dentist's receptionist in the grocery store. You know you know her, but you just can't figure out from *where*, because the setting isn't right. I know I've seen this face somewhere, but it isn't quite right. Something's different, and I can't figure out what it is. If I could just—"

"Shh," Michael said gently. "Don't force it."

"But if I can remember..."

"You will. It'll come back to you." He reached for the telephone. "Meanwhile, I'll get this drawing to the police and see what they come up with—oops, I guess not." He gave her a wry smile and replaced the receiver. "Line's still out. Looks like we're going to have to sit on this for a while."

"Do you realize what this means?" Brady couldn't seem to stop her teeth from chattering. "Somebody I've *seen*, somebody I've come in contact with just going about my business, is trying to—"

"Hey," Michael said, taking her arms, "don't do that." His voice was as rough as his hands were gentle. When Brady only stared at him, he let his breath out in a rush and folded her into his arms. "I know," he said. "I know."

It felt so good—the soft fabric of the sweatshirt under her cheek, and beneath it the steady thumping of his heartbeat. A myriad of feelings, all warm and nameless, blossomed inside her. But before the feelings could generate a response, she felt his lips touch the top of her head, and then he took her arms and put her away from him.

"Well," he said softly, "I guess you're stuck with me." His eyes were warm with understanding and creased at the corners with a fan of delicate lines.

Brady mumbled, "Looks that way." She was thinking that she ought to offer to drive him home—or at least to the nearest telephone. She knew he probably wouldn't ask it of her, he was too reserved, too polite. But she didn't want to offer.

"Well," Michael said, "don't let me get in your way. Just do what you were planning to do." He continued to look down at her, the expression in his dark eyes unreadable.

"Actually," Brady said, licking her lips, "I hadn't made any plans." The world seemed to stop for a second.

And then Michael said, "Oh," and the creases at the corners of his eyes deepened. "In that case, let's make some, you and I." He reached out and turned the sketchbook over, an emphatic gesture of dismissal. "Now, what do we do with a rainy Saturday? What did you do on rainy Saturdays when you were a kid?"

Brady gazed at him, chewing on her lower lip and hugging herself to hide shivers of wonder. He seemed so light-hearted all of a sudden, as if he'd put aside a heavy burden, and in a very real way, Brady supposed, he had done just that. He seemed younger, carefree. The shell hadn't just cracked—he'd taken it off, at least for a little while. Brady didn't question the miracle; she simply accepted it with joy.

"Gee, I don't know," she said, her voice emerging in a breathless rush. "When I was a kid I always spent Saturdays in the newsroom with Dad—rain or shine. What about you?"

"You know something?" Michael was rubbing his jaw and looking pensive. "I'm not sure I can remember a rainy Saturday."

"Oh, come on."

"Listen, where I grew up, it didn't often rain on *any* day of the week."

"Where was that?" Brady asked, fascinated.

"Oh, a little town in the Mojave Desert—no place you've ever heard of. Great weather—cold in the winter, pure hell in the summer, and the wind blows all year round." His mouth had a wry twist, and Brady had an idea his childhood wasn't a place he cared to visit often in memory.

He gave a short laugh. "But I do remember that Saturday was cooking and laundry day. It was my mother's day off—she worked as a waitress in a truck stop. On Saturday she'd do the cooking and washing for the whole week, and all us kids—my two brothers, my sister and I—had to help."

Faintly, afraid of halting the flow of reminiscence, Brady asked, "Was that where you learned to cook?"

"One of the places, I guess." He smiled ruefully. "Though I think about the only thing I ever really learned was how to bake cookies."

"Cookies?" The word burst from her on the crest of an incredulous giggle. It was so completely mind-boggling, trying to imagine Michael—Judge Snow—in an apron, rolling out cookie dough.

"Yeah, my younger brother and I were great cookiemakers, the best...."

His voice trailed off, and his gaze rested almost casually on Brady's mouth. For some reason her lips began to feel almost swollen.

"Well," she said brightly. "You want to cook something now?"

He gave a bark of skeptical laughter. "I don't know— those cupboards of yours didn't look too promising."

Brady lifted her shoulders in an elaborate shrug. "Where there's milk and eggs, there's hope. Didn't somebody say that once?"

"Somebody did," he admitted, looking doubtful. "All right, shall we give it a shot?"

"Sure, why not?"

"Then after you, m'dear." He waved her airily ahead of him into the kitchen.

"Wonders never cease," he said a few minutes later. Brady pulled her head out of a nearby cupboard and found him staring down at a cylindrical container he was holding in his hand. There was a rapt expression on his face. "Oatmeal," he breathed, lifting his eyes to hers. "Do you know what this means?"

"Porridge for breakfast?" Brady ventured.

"Oatmeal cookies!"

"Oatmeal cookies?"

"Do you know how long it's been since I've eaten an honest-to-goodness homemade oatmeal cookie?"

"Why," Brady asked dazedly, "would you *want* to?"

Michael just stared at her. "Do you mean to tell me you've never tasted oatmeal cookies? What kind of childhood did you have, anyway?"

"Deprived, obviously. I had to make do with stale doughnuts and coffee in paper cups."

"Listen, the oatmeal cookies my brother and I made were this big, and flat and chewy. We always fought about whether or not to put raisins in—I hated raisins, my brother loved 'em. I was bigger, so I generally won. And if we were really lucky we had walnuts.''

"What?" Brady murmured. "No chocolate chips?"

Michael gave her a withering glance. "Sheer sacrilege," he snorted. "That's it—we've got to make oatmeal cookies. This will be a day you'll never forget."

The funny thing was that Brady was inclined to agree with him, though for reasons that had nothing whatever to do with oatmeal cookies.

"Um," she said doubtfully, "I don't think I have a recipe."

"Who needs one?" Michael gave a blithe wave and disappeared into a cupboard. "All we need is flour, salt, brown sugar—"

"Oops," Brady said.

Michael withdrew from the cupboard. "No brown sugar?" He looked so disappointed that Brady had to clamp a hand across her mouth to stop the giggles.

"Sorry," she said, choking. Then, as inspiration struck, she snapped her fingers and cried, "Mrs. Wu!"

"I beg your pardon?" Michael said, looking affronted.

"My neighbor, Mrs. Wu. She's a terrific cook. I know she'll have anything we need—she's Italian."

"Mrs. Wu is Italian?"

"Sure, she's only Chinese by marriage. Come on, let's us go a-borrowin', as my dad would say. Get your umbrella!"

"I seem to have lost my umbrella," Michael said after a brief silence, and for just a moment the carefree mood was obscured by the dark clouds of reality that they both knew hovered just a telephone call away.

Brady gave herself a determined little shake and said, "Hey, no sweat. Who needs an umbrella? You can wear Dad's slicker. I think I've got a windbreaker with a hood somewhere."

They dressed for the excursion with excited anticipation, like children venturing out in the season's first snowfall.

They took a shortcut to the Wu's house, running across the hillside, slipping and sliding on the saturated ground. They leaped small gullies full of surging brown water and laughed with the kind of abandon adults rarely allow themselves because it makes them feel undignified, irresponsible and vaguely guilty.

"Don't panic if she hugs you," Brady whispered to Michael as they stood on the Wus' porch, shaking off raindrops and waiting for someone to answer their knock. "Mrs. Wu hugs everybody."

"That's okay," Michael said placidly. "I like hugs."

Brady made an involuntary hiccuping sound and rushed on, hoping her sudden breathlessness would be attributed to physical exertion. "Wait till you meet these two—they're the oddest couple. Absolutely nothing in common. Mr. Wu is a professor at UCLA—economics, I think. Anyway, he's so reserved he calls his wife 'Mrs. Wu.' *She* calls *him* 'Wu,' at least in public. Lord knows what she calls him in private. She'll probably ask us to stay for lunch, but we don't have to. She'll act mortally wounded, but she gets over things quick—Hello, Mrs. Wu!"

Michael thought he'd trained himself well enough not to form expectations before all the facts were in, but Mrs. Wu was a surprise. The woman who stood in the wide-open doorway was large, but stately rather than fat. Her hair was short, dark and worn in a very elegant, up-to-date style. It was swept back from her face, highlighting a two-inch strip of pure white just above the left ear. She was wearing black slacks and a turquoise suede shirt caught at the waist with a belt of Navajo silver. Her face was smooth, her eyes were dark, and her mouth, at the moment, was hanging open.

"Well—" she said, following a silence that lasted for several seconds, "for heaven's sake, would you look at this! Brady Flynn, what are you doing out in this weather! Come in here before you catch pneumonia!"

Brady all but disappeared into a bear hug, wet windbreaker and all. Michael heard her gasp, "Hi, Mrs. Wu.
This is my friend Michael." A moment later he, too, was
enveloped.

"Hello, Michael....*Whoa*—" Still holding on to his arms,
Mrs. Wu leaned back to peer at him. "You're a big one,
aren't you! It sure isn't often I get to look up at a man! Well,
don't just stand there, come in, come in! You think a big
strong man can't get pneumonia? Here, let me take that wet
slicker."

Brady made a "What did I tell you?" face at him as she
preceded him through the doorway.

"Wu's in the library; he's probably reading, but I don't
think he'd notice if you turned on the football game. You're
staying for lunch, of course."

"Uh, actually, we just came to borrow—" Brady began.

Michael stopped in the library doorway, sniffing. He'd
just caught a whiff of the most incredible odor. With hope-
ful reverence he murmured, "Mrs. Wu, do you mind if I
ask, what is that wonderful aroma?"

Mrs. Wu lit up like a Christmas tree. Kissing the tips of
her fingers, she intoned, "Fettuccine with red clam sauce."

Michael closed his eyes. "Ah . . ."

"You like Italian food? So did Sean—that's Brady's father, God rest his soul. He was crazy about my fettuccine.
That settles it—you stay for lunch!"

Beyond her shoulder, Brady was making frantic gestures
and mouthing the word "No," but Michael ignored her.
"That sounds great. Thank you. Is there anything I can help
you with?"

"Oh, no, no, you just go on in the library and watch the
football game. Brady, you come help me with the salad.
Michael—" Mrs. Wu's voice dropped to a hush. "This is a
salad you could die for—romaine lettuce, black olives,
mushrooms marinara and my own special Italian dressing.

Come, Brady, we'll put on the coffeepot and visit in the kitchen.''

"Coffee?" Michael said wonderingly. "Real coffee?"

"I'll bring some in for you when I take Wu his tea."

"Thank you," Michael breathed. "That would be wonderful." He'd just decided that if heaven was an Italian kitchen, he wouldn't mind dying.

Brady gave him a black look and elbowed him as she passed. Out of the side of her mouth, she hissed, "For this I may kill you myself!"

"Why? I thought—"

"I *hate* Italian food, that's why!"

Michael stared at her. "How could anybody hate Italian food?"

"Easy—if you don't like garlic, tomatoes, vinegar or mushrooms!"

"You're kidding! Well, small wonder. You've destroyed your palate with fast food. Hey, what about pizza? You mean to tell me a fast-food junkie like you doesn't like pizza?"

Her furious response was interrupted by an aria from the kitchen. "Bra-dy? Darling, are you coming?"

Brady made a growling noise, threw him a look of frustration and flounced off. Michael watched her go, following the bounce and swing of her ponytail with fascination. He was smiling as he turned into the library to present himself to his unsuspecting host. This weekend was turning out to be full of surprises.

"I like this one," Mrs. Wu said in a loud whisper, nudging Brady a couple of times in the ribs as she passed her on the way to the pantry.

Lunch was over, and Brady and Mrs. Wu were back in the kitchen, the only place for a good feminine heart-to-heart. Brady was rinsing dishes while Mrs. Wu cleared away the leftovers.

"A good man," Mrs. Wu went on sagely. "A *real* man— mature. Just what you need, somebody mature and responsible."

"Shh!" Brady threw a nervous glance toward the door. Over lunch Michael and Mr. Wu had become embroiled in a genteel debate on the long-term effects of Middle Eastern unrest on global economics. They had retired with their argument and a hot drink to the library. Brady knew very well that they couldn't hear, but her cheeks turned red with embarrassment anyway. "It isn't anything like that. I hardly know him."

"Uh-huh, and the next thing you'll tell me is that those aren't Sean's clothes and a day's growth of beard he's wearing, and that he didn't spend the night at your house." Coming out of her spacious pantry, Mrs. Wu raised her eyebrows at Brady and pointedly added, *"Hmm?"*

Brady coughed and said faintly, "It was unintentional; he got stranded. Because of the phone being out."

"Yours, too? I suppose the power will go next. I swear, every time it rains, or the Santa Ana winds blow—oh, well. Listen, Brady, you don't have to explain a thing to me. You're a grown woman, and I'm not your mother—although I don't think even your father, God rest his soul, would have minded too much. He would have liked Michael—I know he would have. That's a man you can trust." She tapped herself in the general vicinity of the heart. "I know it in here." Mrs. Wu nodded with somber emphasis and added, "You could trust that man with your *life*. And, God knows, you shouldn't be living all alone like you do; you know I worry about you. The canyon isn't what it used to be. It's always had its share of weird ducks, but at least they used to be harmless weirdos—flower children and the like. Now I'm not so sure. I think your father would be happy to know you've found such a nice, steady, dependable man. What does he do?"

Caught off guard, Brady could only stammer, "D-do?"

"Yes, for a living. Oh, no, don't tell me—"

"He's in law," Brady said hastily, hoping Mrs. Wu wouldn't notice the evasion.

She needn't have worried. "A lawyer!" Mrs. Wu crowed happily. "Marvelous. No wonder he got on so well with Wu; I think lawyers have orderly minds."

"Mrs. Wu," Brady said firmly, belatedly attempting to salvage the conversation, "it really isn't anything like that. Michael and I are *just friends*." And isn't *that* a lame and well-worn disclaimer? she thought scornfully.

What *were* she and Michael? They couldn't be called friends, they were barely even acquaintances. Just a couple of strangers, in fact, thrown together by circumstance; two bits of debris cast up on the same beach. The thought made her feel inexplicably depressed.

"Well, I think that's that," she said as she put the last dish in the dishwasher and closed it. She took a deep breath and turned, wiping her hands on a towel. "It sure was nice of you to invite us to stay for lunch." She mentally lifted her eyes heavenward, hoping lightning wouldn't strike her for such a lie. The fact was, she'd known Mrs. Wu practically all her life and so far had managed to keep her from even suspecting that she detested the very *smell* of tomato sauce.

"It was my pleasure. I loved having the company. Wu isn't much fun once he gets his nose in a book. In fact, are you sure you can't—"

"We'd better get back while we can still see," Brady said hastily. "It gets dark so early, and I didn't leave a light on. We just came down to—" She snapped her fingers. "Oh, shoot, I almost forgot what we came for! We just came to ask if we could borrow a cup of sugar."

Mrs. Wu gave a snort of laughter. "You're kidding!"

"No, I'm not. I'm serious." Then a chortle burst from her. "We were going to make cookies."

"Brady Flynn, you never baked anything in your life!"

"Well, Michael was, actually."

Mrs. Wu stared at her openmouthed. In hushed tones she said, "This is more than serious—it's a miracle."

They were still laughing when Michael came in to see if Brady was ready to go home. He supervised the selection of the items they would need for the cookies: brown sugar, butter, cinnamon, nutmeg, baking powder and soda. Obviously impressed, Mrs. Wu packed everything in a plastic bag, tied a knot in the end and placed the package reverently in Michael's hands.

She reluctantly brought them their coats and sent them on their way with a hug and a wave, then stood shivering in the doorway, calling after them into the premature twilight, "Hurry, now, but watch your step; it's getting slippery out there! Don't catch cold! Come back soon."

With the onset of the November dusk, the rain seemed to come down harder than ever. It was colder, too, and the small gullies they'd jumped over with ease earlier in the day had become wider and deeper.

About the second time they came to one of the wide ones, when Brady put her foot down she felt the bank crumble beneath it. With a shriek of dismay she plunged knee-deep into churning brown water. Michael grabbed her before she fell, but when he hauled her back to firmer ground her tennis shoe stayed behind in the mud.

Brady squeaked, "My shoe!" and reached for it—too late. They both stood watching the shoe bob away on the crest of the thick chocolate waves, Brady swearing under her breath as only an Irishman—or his daughter—can.

Michael gave her a look that was half admiring, half scandalized. Brady scowled at him and muttered, "Well, *damn*." There being absolutely nothing else she could do, she hunched her shoulders inside her windbreaker and began to pick her way unevenly and painstakingly across the slope.

"Wait," Michael said. Brady turned to look at him. His eyes were no more than shadows inside the slicker's hood. "Come here—get on my back."

Brady said, "What?"

"Come on, get on my back. I'll give you a ride."

Brady stared up at him, blinking rain out of her eyes. "You'll give me a what?"

"A ride. Piggyback. Hurry up. It's getting dark."

"You're not serious."

"Of course I'm serious. What's the matter, haven't you ever been carried piggyback before?"

"Yeah, when I was *six*."

"Then you remember how it's done. Come on, give me your hand."

His voice held a note of command that made further argument seem pointless. Muttering, "I don't believe I'm doing this," Brady took the hand he was extending.

"Now hop up. That's it, put your legs around me and hold on."

"Your slicker's slippery. I can't—"

"Lean forward more. Put your arms around me—*not my neck!* You'll choke me to death. There . . . like that. That's perfect. Now just relax and keep your center of gravity forward, against my back." He crossed his arms to make a support for her bottom and began to plod steadily across the hillside, easily spanning the gullies with his long legs.

Brady thought, I don't believe this. She had an urge—half-hysterical, she supposed—to shout out loud with laughter. It was so silly, but exciting. A little like being scared out of her wits on a roller coaster. Her heart was pounding; she knew he must feel it hammering against his broad back. She could hear the harsh sound of his breathing.

Michael's shoes crunched on flagstones. Brady knew they were on her front walk and that she could get down now.

She knew she ought to; she must be heavy. Michael would be relieved.

But for some reason he made no move to set her down. Instead she felt him mount the steps to her front porch. She felt him turn his head slightly, touching her cheek with his stubbly one.

"Keys," he said hoarsely.

"It's not locked."

"What?"

"I never lock it."

He pulled back his head to stare at her. Brady experienced a peculiar wave of dizziness. She caught her lower lip in her teeth and shrugged apologetically. Michael shook his head and opened the door.

"Light switch?"

"On the right."

"Got it—uh-oh."

They listened to the click of the switch, then listened to it once more, just to be sure.

"Oh, dear," Brady sighed. "I was afraid of that."

"Power's out now, too?"

"Uh-huh."

"Hmm."

"Michael, don't you think you'd better put me down?"

"Oh, yeah, right."

Brady heard the bag of groceries settle to the wooden floor with a muffled "thump." Michael unfolded his arms, leaving her unsupported. His hands took hers in a cool, firm grasp. Reluctantly she unlocked her legs from his waist and straightened them, and in a smooth, graceful motion slid down Michael's back until her feet touched the floor.

But somehow that smooth, graceful motion didn't stop there. It became part of a pas de deux that carried her around Michael's body and into his arms.

Brady gripped his shoulders and stared up into the shadow that was Michael's face. For the space of a few heartbeats they stood like statues, and then Michael muttered something in a harsh undertone—a curse, or a prayer. The hood of his slicker fell back, and one of his hands jerked the hood of Brady's windbreaker off and buried itself in her hair.

A bolt of something powerful and frightening shot through her, forcing a sharp gasp from her throat and creating havoc in her chest. There was such strength in his hands, and so much tension in his body, as if a tremendous struggle were going on inside him. Breathlessly she waited to see whether he would kiss her or cast her from him; either way, she sensed that there would be violence in the act.

At last Michael's fingers moved in her hair, burrowed deep and then tightened. He made a low sound, full of frustration and longing, and brought his mouth down to cover hers. The battle was over, and Brady had no way of knowing whether it had been won—or lost.

And yes, there *was* violence, but it was all internal. His lips were gentle, his mouth didn't crush or bruise, and yet she felt bludgeoned. The sensations were purest heaven—honeyed warmth, the caress of satin and the feather-light touch of fingertips against her skin—but inside her was churning agony. There was a terrible aching in her throat, a burning corkscrew in the pit of her stomach, throbbing heat in the core of her body and spreading weakness in her legs. She offered her mouth to him willingly, welcoming the explorations of his tongue with eagerness and joy, and yet she felt invaded. And as she opened to him still more, inviting greater intimacy and deeper penetration, she heard herself make a sound she'd never made before—a whimpering gasp of helplessness and surrender.

Michael heard the sound, and it only served to intensify the battle that raged inside him. He recognized it for what it was—a cry of raw feminine need. With the part of him that wasn't yet completely out of control, he regretted having brought her to this, even while another part of him—

something savage and primitive in the deepest core of his being—responded to it with a surge of masculine triumph.

Dormant passions were springing to life all through him. Not only was he no longer fully in control, but he suddenly realized that he didn't *want* to be. There was a kind of release in letting go; it was almost a relief to give in and let himself be carried away by his emotions. He discovered that it had been a strain, always being in control, and that it felt good, so good, just to let go.

His world was shrinking, until at last it came down to just himself and this woman. There was no world outside this room, no sprawling city filled with pain and violence, no courts, no criminals, no victims, no demented assassin trying to annihilate him. The room itself didn't exist, except as a tiny cocoon of quiet in the eye of the storm. His existence consisted of himself, his own body and all its senses, and the woman whose presence filled those senses. And of that presence he only wanted *more*.

Her skin was cool, fresh and rain-washed; her hair was thick, heavy and unexpectedly soft, and her mouth was warm, vibrant and so responsive. But it was only the tip of the iceberg, and he wanted to explore the rest. He wanted to discover her body's secrets, its warm hollows and soft, round fullnesses, the places where her pulse would jump like a wild thing when he touched it with his tongue. And more than anything in the world he wanted to immerse himself in her hot, sweet depths and for a few brief moments, at least, lose himself there....

Then Fate, with just the slightest of twitches, chose to call a halt to his little excursion into irresponsibility. The twitch came in the form of a sound—a very small sound, but one so out of place that it resounded like a rifle shot through his consciousness. In an instant it shattered his cocoon of blissful oblivion, and reality came surging in upon him like a tidal wave. The fine hairs on the back of his neck lifted and stirred, and muscles contracted in the small of his back.

His entire body became intent, every nerve and fiber poised, *listening*, like a wild animal that senses the presence of the predator.

Somewhere in the darkness outside, above the rushing of the rain, he had heard the unmistakable crunch of a shoe on gravel.

Chapter 6

He heard Brady say his name. "Michael..."

He silenced her with a sharp hiss, and then, realizing that he must be hurting her, he loosened his grip on her hair and rubbed her scalp with his fingertips in mute apology. With every nerve on red alert, he waited for the sound to repeat itself.

Brady stirred restively in his arms, but remained silent. With his lips touching her ear he whispered, "Someone's outside. I heard—"

Footsteps scraped loudly on flagstone, then stomped forthrightly up the front porch steps. A feminine voice with a husky edge called, "Brady? Are you in there? Is everything okay?"

"Oh, thank God." Brady sagged against him and rested her forehead momentarily on his chin. "It's only the Sunshines."

"The *what*?"

"My neighbors." She turned her head, calling with a curiously gentle reassurance in her voice. "Yes, Shyla, I'm here. I'm fine."

Michael whispered wonderingly, *"Shyla Sunshine?"*

Brady gave a breathy laugh. "Yeah, try saying that more than once in a row. And if you think that's bad, her husband's name is Sky. Mrs. Wu calls them the Sunshine Twins, but they're not. They're married—I think—and I don't think Sunshine is their real name, either."

"No, really?"

There was another of those whispery giggles. "They're okay, just a little bit—well, it isn't like they aren't playing with a full deck so much, it's more like they don't even know what game it is. It's like they got stuck in the Age of Aquarius. They used to live in this commune, but now they live in a trailer up the hill. They keep goats and chickens. They give me milk and eggs and all these organically grown vegetables. I guess technically they're squatters, and every so often someone tries to get rid of them, but I think they're kind of sweet, actually."

"Brady? Are you sure you're okay?"

"They worry about me," Brady murmured, and sighed. She moved in a reluctant sort of way, and, equally reluctant, Michael let her go.

She opened the door, murmuring greetings and reassurances in that curiously tender voice. The two silhouetted shapes on the porch merged with Brady's. This had to be, Michael thought, the huggingest bunch of people he'd ever seen.

"This is my friend Michael," Brady said.

Two voices, indistinguishable from one another, murmured, "Hi, Michael." The voices had a breathless quality that was almost childlike. Michael began to be curious about what these people looked like.

"We didn't see any lights," one of the voices said to Brady. The other one added, "We knew you were home; we saw your car."

The first voice took over once more. "When the electricity went out, and we didn't see any lights—"

"We thought maybe you didn't have any candles—"

"—so we brought you some."

"Thank you," Brady said softly. "That's really nice of you. We were—Michael and I just got home. We were down at Mrs. Wu's."

"Oh!" Both voices had a smile in them. Both silhouetted heads bobbed up and down. "Were you? That's really nice."

There was a rustling sound, and the faint clacking of wax candles bumping against each other. Brady murmured, "Thanks, I haven't even had a chance to see if I have any yet. Can you come in for a minute?"

"Oh, no." The two silhouettes floated toward the door. "We have to get back. The goats need to be milked. Do you need anything? Can we bring you anything? Are you out of milk yet?"

"No, that's all right. Maybe tomorrow, okay?"

"Okay." The voices were cheerful and happy. "We'll bring you some tomorrow. The persimmons are ripe; would you like us to bring you some of those, too?"

"Sure," Brady murmured. "That'd be great."

"Okay, see you tomorrow. Take care, now."

"You too. Bye."

The door closed with a whisper. Michael stood regarding the empty darkness in fascinated silence.

"Well," Brady said, "see what I mean?"

Michael said, "Good Lord."

"I know, aren't they incredible? And the funny thing is, they really are that sweet. They're so sweet they don't even know that the rest of the world *isn't*. It sort of makes you want to keep them from finding out."

In the darkness Michael turned his head toward her, and for a few moments he didn't say anything. He wondered if she could possibly know how she touched him. She was just so damned *unexpected*. Nearly everything about her surprised him, but what surprised him the most was how much he was beginning to *like* her. And he didn't know why—they had nothing in common beyond their jobs. They had nothing on which to base a friendship, nothing to talk about. And yet, somehow, they did seem to talk, and he didn't know when he'd enjoyed anyone's company so much.

For a moment longer he listened to Brady moving with assurance through her dark living room. Then, partly out of curiosity and partly to distract himself from the disquieting nature of his thoughts, he asked, "What do they do? How do they make a living? Just by raising goats and chickens and organic vegetables?"

"Oh, no, they give that stuff away. No, Sky works at this halfway house for junkies in Santa Monica. Shyla's into stained glass. She makes things and takes them to craft fairs. You know, like they have on the boardwalk at Venice. I guess they didn't go this weekend because of the rain."

There was a hissing sound, and the gas log came on, softly outlining the shapes in the room. By its meager illumination he saw that Brady was searching through a small drawer full of odds and ends—for matches, he imagined. Since he didn't smoke and couldn't help her out, he just stood and watched her. When she finally located a book of matches and lit one, he saw that she'd laid out an assortment of objects that had obviously already seen a lot of duty as makeshift candle holders: beer bottles, chipped saucers, jar lids, even a pair of rather beautiful brass candlesticks.

"Tell me," he said, watching the play of firelight across her cheek, "just out of curiosity, what do they look like, these flower children of yours?"

She'd been absorbed in what she was doing, lighting the candles one by one, tilting them to make puddles of melted wax, setting them in their makeshift holders. Now she looked up and smiled, the lighted candle in her hand making tiny flickering flames in her eyes. From somewhere in the attic of his mind a phrase came to Michael: *Bell, Book and Candle*. And for just a moment, in that whispery golden ambience of rain and candlelight, he really did wonder if she could be a witch.

Suddenly it seemed much too warm to be wearing a slicker. He took it off and hung it over the back of a chair.

"They look just alike," Brady said, laughing softly. "Except Sky has a beard, and his hair is longer."

She was moving around the room, placing candles on tabletops and windowsills. When the last one had been set out, she turned to survey the room, then glanced at Michael. She made a jerky, nervous gesture with her hands, as if she didn't know quite what to do next. Then, as if only just remembering that she was still wearing it, she unzipped her windbreaker and shrugged out of it. Slowly, carefully, not looking at Michael, she pulled the purple scarf off and combed her hair with her fingers. The fire and candlelight made it shine like polished brass; watching her, Michael wondered what had ever made him think it wouldn't be soft to touch.

The silence became almost visible—thick and pervasive, like fog. Brady cut through it finally by clearing her throat and saying, "Well." Her voice seemed unnaturally loud. "What would you like to do now?"

"We can still make cookies," Michael pointed out. "Your stove is gas."

"Oh, all right. I guess we could do that."

They both reached for the bag of groceries Mrs. Wu had given them. Brady's hand touched Michael's. She snatched it back, straightened abruptly and stood for a moment, rubbing her hand on her thigh. She muttered, "I'll go turn on the oven," and fled.

Michael, watching her go, thought, What have I done?

In the kitchen Brady was thinking, What am I doing?

She told herself that she was acting like a stupid teen-ager. It wasn't as if she'd never been alone with a man before.

Yeah, maybe, but this was different. She didn't exactly know why; she just knew it *was*. Michael was different. She didn't know what to say to him, how to deal with him. He was completely out of her league. That was what she told herself, and to make herself believe it, all she had to do was close her eyes and concentrate on the image of Judge Snow on the bench, wearing his black robes and that look of benign indifference. His George Washington look—full of wisdom and dignity and unassailable authority.

The only trouble was that unless she concentrated very hard that image kept getting supplanted in her mind's eye by others that were more recent and a lot more vivid. Michael unshaven, Michael asleep, or Michael, his eyes twinkling, with a little fan of lines around their corners. Michael as he was right this minute, licking cookie dough off the ball of his thumb. . . .

"Want a taste?" he asked her, offering the mixing spoon. She shook her head.

And then, if she wasn't careful, she'd start to *feel* things. Things like the gentle tug and pull of his fingers in her hair, the firm, warm satin of his lips touching hers with a wordless question, the way his tongue felt, moving against hers, invading all her senses. She'd start to hear the way his heartbeat sounded against her ear, and the way her own hammered inside her chest when he held her. . . .

"Come on," Michael insisted, smiling. "Humor me. Make like a birdie."

A shivery giggle burst from her as she opened her mouth and let him put a morsel of dough on her tongue. "Mmm," she murmured, incapable of further comment. Michael beamed and looked smug.

It was feelings that made things so confusing. Because when his arms were around her and his hands were tangled in her hair and his mouth was invading hers so gently, he just didn't seem awesome. He seemed like a man. Not a monument out of reach on some cold pedestal, but a man with warm blood surging through his veins, a man capable of passion as well as compassion. A man she could love. Even, just possibly, a man who needed her.

He needs me. The realization came to Brady as she watched Michael drop blobs of dough onto a cookie sheet. Or at least he needs this—a place he can feel at home in, someplace where he can let his defenses down, where he doesn't always have to be all-knowing, always in control. She suddenly remembered the terrible isolation she had sensed in him only moments before a speeding car had shattered it all to smithereens. And she thought, He needs to trust someone.

"Here," Michael said. "Your turn."

Brady stared at him. He gave her a look of exasperation. "Come on, it's simple—all in the wrist. I'll show you."

Brady caught her lower lip in her teeth and let him give her a spoon. As he did so, he covered her hand with his big, warm one.

Michael trusts me. That realization struck her almost like a physical blow, stunning her. Michael trusted her. She didn't know why; she had an idea he didn't even know it himself. But he had let her see him without his armor— barefoot and unshaven and vulnerable—and for a man like Michael to do that, he *must* trust her.

"There, I think you're getting the hang of it," Michael said, smiling down at her.

Brady just looked at him, overcome by recent revelations, overwhelmed by both his nearness and the need to be even closer to him. She wanted to be held again, to be kissed again; she wanted it so badly that it scared her. It was filling her up, leaving no room for air, making her light-headed.

And at the same time she had the frustrating feeling that even if he did let go of his self-control long enough to kiss her, he'd only pull back again, leaving her tied in knots.

The strain was becoming unbearable. In sudden panic Brady thought, I can't stand this! Shivers slid down her spine, then darted through her body in all directions. She knew Michael felt them, because he suddenly gave her an odd, unreadable look and let go of her hand. He moved away from her, making it seem natural by putting the cookie sheet into the oven, then gathering up the dirty dishes and putting them in the sink. Carefully keeping busy. Keeping the distance between them.

Brady looked desperately at the clock on the stove and thought in dismay, What are we going to do with the rest of this evening?

It wasn't much comfort to remember belatedly that the clock was electric, and that the only information it had to give was the precise moment of the power failure.

"Well," Brady inquired of the back of Michael's neck, "what do you want to do now?" Her voice seemed unnaturally hoarse.

Michael turned around and leaned against the sink, drying his hands on a dish towel. It occurred to him that any answer he could possibly make would be as blatant an evasion as he'd ever told. Every nerve in his body was tingling with impulses he knew he had to deny, so he said dryly, "Since video games appear to be out of the question, what about cards?"

Brady brightened and said hopefully, "Poker?" His expression must have been very revealing, because she went on, looking pained, "Okay, then, what *do* you play? Oh, no, don't tell me—*bridge?*"

"As a matter of fact," Michael said loftily, "I do play occasionally. But since neither bridge nor poker works well with two players, how about—"

"Gin rummy!"

Michael groaned. "I haven't played since college. What terrible memories that brings back."

"I'll get the cards," Brady said breathlessly, racing out of the room.

When she came out of her father's bedroom carrying a deck of cards and wearing a green eyeshade, Michael said, "Uh-oh, I think I'm in trouble."

Brady said, "Shut up and cut the cards."

"Gin," she said sometime later. "And that makes . . . ninety-four dollars you owe me."

"Shark," Michael muttered. "Settle for a cookie?" he asked hopefully, offering her the last one on the plate.

"No, thanks, I'm stuffed. You know what I just realized? We didn't have any dinner."

"Sure we did—oatmeal cookies and goat's milk." Michael contemplated the last cookie for a moment, then sighed and bit into it. That softness around his middle was going to cost him anyway; he might just as well enjoy being out of shape. "I've had worse meals, and I *know* you have."

"What's that supposed to mean? Have I just been insulted?"

Michael just snorted, grinned and said, "Greaseburgers?"

She grinned back sheepishly and shrugged. Her gaze caught his and stayed there, and that was probably a mistake. Fascinated, he watched the focus of her eyes sharpen, then intensify. The silence began to echo.

She stood abruptly and walked slowly toward one of the front windows. The candle there was guttering; she licked her fingers and deftly snuffed the flame, then stood looking out at the darkness, rubbing absently at her upper arms.

"Is it still raining?" Michael asked softly.

"Yes." He saw her shoulders lift and settle. "It seems like it's been raining forever."

"It hasn't. It's only been a little more than twenty-four hours since it started. Yesterday."

"Just yesterday." She rubbed harder at her arms, and Michael knew that what she was feeling was the prickle of gooseflesh. He felt it himself. Just yesterday they had both come within a split second of a particularly ugly and violent death. They'd been strangers then. What were they now?

Looking at her, at the defensive set of her slender shoulders, the vulnerable angle of her head and neck, the hair that captured and held the firelight, Michael felt the ground shift beneath his feet, as if his world were being rocked by a small earthquake. He felt another of those surges of anger—anger that some nameless assassin should have the power to create such upheaval in him. The assassin had introduced fear into his world, and fear had brought anger in its wake. Somehow those passions had opened the floodgates; he wasn't in control anymore. Not of his life, his fate, his destiny—not even of his own emotions. He hated the feeling of being off balance, out of control. He wanted to feel solid ground under his feet again.

"Brady," Michael said gently, "if the phone is still on the blink tomorrow, I'll figure something else out. I never intended to move in on you like this. You've been very nice about it, and I can't tell you how much I've appreciated—"

"Hey!" She turned around and skewered him with her eyes. "Don't, okay?" Her face was tense, unsmiling.

He looked at her for a moment, then nodded and murmured, "All right." He saw her swallow, shrug and painfully try a laugh. And he had to tuck his hands into his armpits to keep from going over and putting his arms around her.

Almost defensively she said, "You know, it's weird, but I've really been having fun."

Fun. He played the concept over in his mind a couple of times. "You know what's even weirder? So have I." He considered that with a growing sense of wonder. "Do you know how long it's been since I've done something just for *fun*?"

"Maybe you should try it more often." Her voice had acquired a breathless quality, her cheeks an underlying glow of pink. Michael began to find the habit she had of catching her lower lip with her teeth when she was slightly embarrassed utterly fascinating. "You...um...you don't have to leave. You know you could stay as long as you—"

"No!" The harshness of his voice shocked him. He cleared his throat and said a little more gently, "Brady, I really think I'd better go, don't you?" When she just went on looking at him with that searing blue gaze, he let his breath out in a gust of frustration and rubbed his jaw with his hands. The whispery rasp of a day's growth of beard came as a surprise. He stared at his fingers and muttered, "Good Lord."

"If you wanted to shave, you should have said so. I could have loaned you a razor."

She sounded so belligerent that he had to smile at her. "What's the matter, don't you like the rumpled look? I thought—"

"I like it fine." Her voice was flat with tension.

Michael's smile faded. "Brady..."

She made a sudden movement, pushing herself away from the window. She didn't come near him, but instead sat stiffly on one corner of the hearth and drew her knees up to her chest. When she spoke, her voice had the same jerkiness as her movements, as if, Michael thought, she were quaking inside.

"Look, I have to tell you, I'm having some trouble with this."

Michael frowned and murmured, "What?" even though he knew very well.

"With us—you and me. What's happened between us. Look, maybe you can deal with it by ignoring it, but I can't. I'm sorry. I just really need to understand what's going on."

"Going on?" He was stalling for time.

"Yeah, with you. I need to know—"

"Where I'm coming from?" Michael felt an ironic smile touch his face and instantly erased it. She didn't deserve that. She didn't deserve any of this. He looked at her for a long time, then closed his eyes. "I'm sorry," he said, shaking his head. "I'd like to tell you. I just don't think I can."

"Why not?"

"Because I don't think you'd understand."

Her sharp bark of laughter made him open his eyes, and he saw that she was angry. "You sound like *me*—about fifteen years ago. I used to say that to my dad, and you know something? He never bought it, either! Why do you do that? Why do you try to make it sound like we're from two different generations?"

Michael sighed. "Because we are, Brady."

"The hell we are! I'm sorry, but I'm not a kid, and you're not Methuselah. How old are you, anyway?"

"Forty-two."

"And I'm almost twenty-nine. Thirteen years does not make a generation, Michael!"

"Not in years, maybe. But in attitudes, values . . ."

"What attitudes? What values?"

"Look, we're both products of our upbringing."

"What do you know about my upbringing?"

Michael took a deep breath and tried to speak calmly, reasonably. "You grew up in Los Angeles. This town is probably the do-your-own-thing capital of the world. You grew up in a time and place where there weren't too many restrictions on personal behavior. Your choice of life-styles is unlimited." He paused for another deep breath. Brady kept quiet, but there was a dangerous light kindling in her eyes. "Brady, I grew up in a very small town, in a time when everyone was expected to follow the same set of rules. Attitudes were different then—about a lot of things. I guess some of those attitudes are harder to change on a gut level than they are on an intellectual level.'' He paused, frowning, to ask hopefully, ''Am I making sense?''

''No,'' Brady said in a hard, flat voice. ''But I understand what you're saying. You're telling me that because I've behaved a certain way with you, you think I have a free and easy attitude toward *sex*, right?''

''No, Brady—''

''You think I just jump into the sack with anybody I happen to fancy, right?''

''I wasn't making a judgment,'' he said stiffly. ''Merely an observation.''

''Oh, and you observe that I'm pretty quick to jump into the arms of complete strangers, right?''

She was plainly beyond anger. Her chest was heaving; she looked like a pagan priestess about to call a host of demons down on his head. But at the same time her eyes, her witch's eyes, seemed softer. They weren't stabbing at him like twin daggers. It was only when she touched her nose with the back of her hand and sniffed that he realized the softness was tears.

''I've got news for you, Your Honor.'' The tears didn't show in her voice; it was low, but steady. ''I don't do this sort of thing with just anybody—heck, sometimes I have to know a guy for a whole week before I invite him to bed!''

''Brady...'' That shimmering glaze in her eyes was doing something very uncomfortable to his insides. He knew that she was as confused by all of this as he was. He made a movement toward her, and then, realizing that it would be disastrous to touch her, he held his body rigid and tried instead to gentle her with his voice. ''Brady, that's not what I meant. That's not what I think of you. I meant that you're probably freer to follow your heart, or your instincts, when it comes to sex. You don't carry around all the hang-ups my generation does—the burdens of guilt and responsibility. Do you understand?''

While listening to him talk, she'd turned her head to stare at the play of light and shadow across the hearth. When he finished, she nodded without looking at him, and after a moment took a deep breath and said slowly, "You make it sound like such serious business."

"I guess that's what I'm trying to say," he said gently. "To me, it is."

Now she turned to look at him. "It doesn't *always* have to be serious, does it?"

He found that he couldn't answer her. The gentle sibilance of rain and fire took over the silence.

It was nearly dark in the room; most of the candles had drowned themselves in pools of melted wax. It was dark and warm and intimate, and sitting a couple of feet away was a woman with hair the color of sun-ripe wheat, hair that smelled of rain and felt like silk against his skin. A woman so responsive that she fit his body and moods like a custom-made shirt. A woman he wanted so badly he could taste it.

He thought, Mike, you're crazy. She was offering him solace, a chance to lose himself in her and for a few moments forget about fear and tension, danger and uncertainty. What was the matter with him that he couldn't take what she was offering him and forget about consequences?

Consequences. What about the consequences? Apparently she didn't see anything wrong with it, and neither did he, really. It was the reasons that were wrong. He'd already formed one relationship based on the wrong reasons, and he had lived with the consequences for a long, long time. He didn't want to do it again. He couldn't make love to a woman for the sake of temporary oblivion—at least not this woman. He couldn't use her like that. Not Brady.

A few moments of escape—that was all it would be. Wouldn't it? What else *could* it be? He'd barely known her more than a day.

"Well," Brady said quietly, "where do we go from here?"

It was just too late for him to learn a new set of rules. As quietly as she had spoken, he replied, "There are two doors over there. You're going to go through one of them, and I'm going to go through the other. You're going to get into your bed, and I'm going to get into mine, and we're both going to get a good night's sleep."

It was his sentencing voice—calm and implacable. Brady sat very still for a long moment; then, without a word, she got up, walked into her bedroom and closed the door.

Without her in it, the room wasn't warm and cozy anymore; it was just empty. Michael took a long, deep breath and closed his eyes, then stretched his neck and shoulder muscles as if he'd just been carrying something heavy. He picked up a candle that still had life in it, blew out the few that remained and went into his room.

In the chilly light of the single candle he stood looking at the drawings on the walls—the ones of Brady. A toddler with a mop of curls, clutching a teddy bear with one ear. A little girl with mud on her overalls and the gleam of mischief in her eyes. A tomboy wearing a Los Angeles Dodgers baseball cap, with a gap in her grin. And Michael's favorite: the girl in the prom dress. Sean Flynn had captured a lot in that portrait of his daughter—more than a camera ever could. She had put her hair up in a sophisticated style, but instead of making her look grown-up, it only emphasized the childlike curve of her jaw, the vulnerability of her bare shoulders. There was something very defenseless about the exposed neck, the fragile shell of her ear. She wasn't smiling; her expression was almost sulky, and there was something in her eyes that might have been fear. It was the look of a girl who was about to leave childhood behind forever, and who wasn't at all sure she was ready. She'd been having a lot of fun as a child, and womanhood was a frightening unknown.

Even as a woman, she seemed to have a capacity for fun that was both innate and contagious. With her even he, Judge Michael A. Snow, had had fun, which under the circumstances was nothing short of miraculous. As he'd told her, it had been a long time since he'd done anything just for fun.

As he stood there looking down at the afghan that covered his bed, he suddenly found himself wondering whether he'd ever made love just for the fun of it. In his youth there had probably been too much self-doubt and insecurity, too much need to protect his fragile masculine ego. Certainly with Helen sex had always been a serious business, and since the divorce his few liaisons had been brief and as often as not had left him with nothing but a vague sense of distaste. No, he thought it very unlikely that he'd ever found sex to be much fun.

A series of images flashed before him: Brady wearing a green eyeshade and saying, "Shut up and deal." Brady combing her wet hair with her fingers. Brady catching that wonderfully soft, full lower lip with her teeth to hold back a breathless giggle. Memory exploded through his senses. For a moment he could *feel* the cool velvet of her cheek, the rain in her hair, the textures of her mouth, the eager response in her body....

For a few brief moments, before he disciplined himself to sleep, Michael allowed himself the luxury of imagining that, with Brady, it might be different.

Chapter 7

Brady woke up Sunday morning to the sound of a rooster crowing and knew, even before she opened her eyes, that the rain had stopped.

The world had righted itself; the sun was shining again in Southern California. It was Sunday. Joggers would be out making up for lost time; the legions of L.A. homeless would be soaking up warmth in the grassy malls around City Hall, and along Sunset Boulevard, Star Map signs would be springing up like daffodils.

And Michael would be leaving.

It was interesting, Brady thought, how bleak and lonely the world could seem, despite the sun pouring like liquid gold across the foot of her bed, warming her toes even under the blankets. Funny, in the year since her father had suddenly died of a heart attack, she had never once been lonely. Oh, she had missed Sean—not a day went by that she didn't miss him dreadfully, painfully. But she'd never felt alone. And that, she knew, was because she wasn't alone. She had a lot of really terrific, wonderful friends. People like Kyle and the Sunshines and Mr. and Mrs. Wu. With the help of her friends and her work, the gap in her life had become a bearable pain; the hole would always be there, but the raw edges had healed.

But this morning, with the sun shining and birds singing all around, she was confronting a new and frightening emptiness, one that seemed to stretch into an indefinite future. She saw that future as a vast, waterless plain, hostile and barren. She had to face it alone—and she was thirsty already.

Michael was going; the fantasy was over. It was time to go out into the daylight and face the real world. Tomorrow morning she would walk into a courtroom with her pad and pencils, the bailiff would intone, "All rise," and Michael would come through the door to take his place behind the big high desk—only he wouldn't be Michael. He'd be the Honorable Michael A. Snow, presiding judge. George Washington, Mount Rushmore, something godlike, untouchable. Michael would be just a poignant memory, the kind that lingers after a particularly affecting theatrical performance.

And how long, she wondered, would it take for those memories to fade? How could she ever forget that George Washington had once given her a piggyback ride? That he had soothed her nightmares, fed her cookie dough with his fingers and kissed her until her knees turned to water?

How could a man she'd known for such a short time leave such a big hole in her with his going? How long would it take *this* pain to heal?

She threw back the covers with a sigh, stretched and padded into the bathroom to turn on the water in the shower. She could hear the water running in the other bathroom. This morning the idea that Michael was standing naked under a stream of hot water only inches away seemed neither fantastic nor funny. It just made her ache deep down inside.

She was standing at the sink brushing her teeth when she heard the knock on the front door. It was very loud, and held an urgency that suggested it might have been going on for some time. She'd been in the shower, so she supposed she must have missed it earlier. She gave a groan and tried to holler, "Just a minute."

The knocking turned into pounding. Exasperated, Brady stuck the toothbrush into her mouth, snatched up the T-shirt she'd dropped on the floor and yanked it over her head. Still holding her toothbrush in her hand, she cautiously stuck her head out her bedroom door and called through her toothpaste, "Who is it?"

Kyle's voice loudly drowned her own query. "Brady, are you in there?"

At that moment the door next to hers opened. Michael burst through it, wearing a towel and nothing else. There was a great deal of white lather on his jaws. He was holding a disposable razor and looking tense.

"Brady! Are you okay?" came from outside the house. "Come on, damn it—answer me!"

Michael mouthed the words, "Who is that?" Brady just stared helplessly at him; she couldn't have answered him if she had tried. Michael's bare chest and torso, with their masculine pattern of dark hair, his back and shoulders, still speckled with water drops, all made a more awesome sight than even his judicial robes.

"Brady!" There was muffled swearing from beyond the front door. A second later the door was thrown open; Kyle started through it, then halted, frozen in mid-expletive. Brady suddenly saw the whole room as a tableau, a scene that flashed through her mind in a series of lightning penstrokes. She would have given anything just to capture the expression on Kyle's face.

He was the first to come back to life. Relaxing his stance, he looked from Michael in his towel and lather to Brady with her toothbrush and T-shirt, cleared his throat and said, "Your Honor, ah, good morning, sir."

Brady couldn't even giggle without strangling on toothpaste. She put a hand over her mouth and looked helplessly at Michael. He frowned and said gravely, "Good morning—Kyle Horner, isn't it?"

Kyle waved a hand, then used it to scratch his head. "Yeah ... I'm a friend of Brady's. Look, I'm really sorry. I just got a little worried." He looked accusingly at Brady. "You didn't show up at Sasha's last night, and your phone was out, so I came here. Then I saw your car in the carport, and you didn't answer your door. And you never lock—" He transferred his distracted look to Michael. "Do you know she never locks her door? Can you believe that? Hey, look, I'm sorry. I can see she's in good hands. I'll just, um ..."

Brady put out a hand like a traffic cop and managed a gargled bellow. Michael said mildly, "I think she'd like you to wait a minute. Why don't you close the door and come in?" Brady gave him a grateful look and ran for the bathroom.

When she came back out to the living room a few minutes later, fully dressed, she heard Michael say, "... a little accident leaving the courthouse Friday night."

Kyle's eyes jerked to her face. "You had an accident? Are you okay?"

She glanced at Michael and caught the barely perceptible shake of his head. Puzzled, she murmured, "Oh, yeah, just a couple of bruises."

"She was pretty shaken up, and I didn't feel she was in any shape to drive home in the rain," Michael said blandly.

"Yeah, right," Kyle murmured, still staring intently at Brady.

"I meant to call a cab from here, but the phone was out. Brady was kind enough to offer me her spare room for the duration."

"Michael," Brady said, obscurely piqued, "You don't have to explain."

Kyle's eyebrows went up. Brady could almost hear him asking her, *"Michael?"*

"Well," Michael said, looking down at the razor in his hand, "I'd better be getting dressed. My cab will be here anytime, I imagine. If you'll excuse me..."

"Cab?" Brady said faintly. She felt as if someone had just socked her in the stomach. "When did you call a cab?"

"A few minutes ago. The phone's working again." His voice was very soft, his eyes unreadable. "You were still asleep." He held her gaze for a moment longer, then turned away. The bedroom door closed softly behind him.

Brady swallowed hard and turned back to Kyle. His gaze was on her, shrewd and uncomfortably perceptive. "What's this about an accident?"

She shrugged, then swallowed again. "Pedestrian hit-and-run," she said, lying glibly. "Pretty mundane for downtown L.A., actually. It didn't hit me—Michael pushed me out of the way. Look, no big deal, okay?"

"Okay," Kyle said agreeably. "Sounds like a great story. Judge saves reporter's life." And then, softly: "Why do I get the feeling there's a better one you aren't telling me?"

She opened her mouth and closed it again. She looked toward the closed bedroom door, then down at her bare feet. Kyle murmured, "Come on, I've known you too long." He tapped the end of his nose. "I can always tell when you're holding out on me."

A horn honked down below on the street. Brady drew a quivery breath. Kyle said, "That must be the cab."

Michael came out of the bedroom with his rumpled raincoat and sports jacket over one arm, holding his tie and briefcase in the other hand. "Did I hear a horn?"

Brady nodded and whispered, "Yeah."

"Well, looks like I made it just in the nick of time." He gave her a wry grin.

She nodded and focused her eyes on the second button of his shirt. Kyle cleared his throat and moved to the counter, where he became tactfully engrossed in a pile of magazines.

"Gotta go," Michael murmured. His voice sounded husky.

"I guess you do."

"Thanks—for everything."

Brady shrugged. "For what? Geez, you saved my life."

He just looked at her. Her throat was hot and dry. She wanted to touch him, to say something. There was so much yet to say! *Damn Kyle!* Why did he have to be here *now*?

The horn sounded again impatiently. Michael laughed and said, "Well. Goodbye."

"Goodbye." The words hurt her throat. She laughed, hoping she wouldn't cry. "Hey, don't forget, you owe me ninety-four dollars."

The fan of lines appeared briefly at the corners of his eyes. She felt his fingers on her cheek, the lightest of touches. "See you in court," he murmured, and was gone.

Just like that.

"Looks like you had an interesting weekend," Kyle observed without looking up.

"It's not what you're thinking."

"How do you know what I'm thinking?"

"Come on, Kyle."

"Look, I know a scene fraught with tension when I'm in the middle of one. If you ask me, there were things left unsaid in that little farewell that would make Romeo blush. But hey, that's none of my business, right? What I really want to know about is this little hit-and-run accident of yours—and why His Honor didn't want you to tell me about it." He chuckled at Brady's small, involuntary start. "Yeah, I caught that little exchange. I want the details, babe. And the first thing I want you to tell me is who the hell is *this*?"

He tapped the page of the drawing tablet in his hands, then turned it around for her to see. Brady licked her lips and cleared her throat, stalling for time. "Um, it's just a face. It doesn't have anything to do—"

"Cut it out, Brady. Take a good look at it." Very softly he added, "You always capture *all* the details, don't you?"

Yes, she did. She had. Without even realizing it, she had framed the face of the assassin in a rain-spattered windshield. Below the face, a pair of hands gripped a steering wheel with deadly purpose.

"Is this the person who almost ran you down?"

Brady nodded and whispered, "Yes."

Kyle's eyes narrowed; he no longer looked the least bit boyish. "You actually saw the guy?" He shook his head and tossed the tablet onto the counter. "Then I really don't understand. What didn't Snow want you to tell me? Do you know what I could do with this? We could put this on the six o'clock news and have the guy behind bars tomorrow. What the hell's going on here?"

Brady stared at Kyle. *Put this on the six o'clock news…behind bars tomorrow.* Of course! Hadn't the Night Stalker been caught because of a police artist's sketch?

She had thought the man looked familiar. Chances were someone else would, too—someone who could put a name to the face. Even an address.

Michael hadn't wanted the story made public because he valued his privacy, but that was before they'd had a *face*. If putting that face on television resulted in the assassin's capture, the danger to Michael would be over. He would be safe.

Kyle was waiting for an answer. Brady made her decision. "It wasn't an accident," she said, and took a deep breath. "It was attempted murder."

"Come on, Brady, who'd want to kill you?" Kyle's voice was quiet, but he wasn't smiling, and his eyes were still narrowed and as hard as glass.

"Not me—Michael."

"The judge?"

She nodded. Kyle took out a cigarette and lit it. "He told you?"

She nodded again and added, "The police know. It's happened a couple of times before this. Gunshots, though— not a car."

"Yeah, that'd be more the Gianelli brothers' style," Kyle said thoughtfully, squinting down at the drawing.

"The police don't think it's professional," Brady said, and told him why.

Kyle nodded. "That makes sense. If that's true, and it's not a professional contract, then it's somebody with a grudge—probably somebody with a screw loose." He tapped the drawing. "This would sure be a good way to nail him." He reached for the phone. "Any idea which precinct is handling this?" Brady shook her head. "Well, I'll try Rampart; downtown's as good a place to start as any." He was dialing as he spoke, his cigarette dangling from his lips. Brady went into the kitchen, got an ashtray out of a drawer and slid it across the counter toward him. He caught it deftly, covered the receiver with his hand and muttered, "Got any beer?"

Brady raised her eyebrows and looked pointedly at the clock. "Shall I put an egg in it and call it breakfast?"

Now listening intently, Kyle ignored that. Brady got a beer out of the refrigerator and opened it and then, because her mouth felt so dry, got one for herself, as well.

"Want a glass?" she asked Kyle, who was just hanging up. He shook his head and reached for the bottle. He was looking pleased with himself, the look he always got when he knew he had a shot at an exclusive. "What did you find out?"

"Lieutenant Sanchez at Rampart is not a happy man just now. They've been keeping a tight lid on this thing because of the probable mob connection.'' He chuckled. ''He wants to know who my source is. Badly.''

''Oh,'' Brady said, and pressed her fingers to her lips.

Kyle glanced at her and said soothingly, ''Don't worry, babe; you know I'd go to jail before I'd betray a source. Now then, let's have it all. Everything you know, everything that happened Friday.''

Brady told him everything she knew, but his reassurances had only made her feel worse. She wished he hadn't used the word ''betray.'' She wished she'd had a chance to talk to Michael about this. She kept telling herself that what they were doing was in Michael's best interests, that broadcasting the assassin's picture was the best way to put an end to the danger Michael was in. She was certain she was doing the right thing, but there was a cold, sick feeling in her stomach that said Michael might not agree with her.

''Okay, I think that does it,'' Kyle said, surveying his notes with an air of satisfaction. ''I'll get on this right away. I want to check out a couple of things before I go on the air. I think maybe Monday. Six o'clock news, with station-break lead-ins.'' He went on thinking out loud as he tore the picture out of the tablet and carefully tucked his notebook and pen away. He paused suddenly, frowning at the picture. After a moment he gave his head a little shake.

Feeling chilled, Brady said, ''What?''

He shook his head again. ''Nothing. I just thought this guy looked a little bit familiar, but I guess not. Well, gotta go. I'd like to talk to my street contacts, find out what the word is about a contract on the judge. That'll probably take a day or two, though. Damn. Hey, don't worry.'' He leaned over to kiss her cheek and tweak a strand of her hair. ''This is hot, babe, great story. You done good. Take care, now. See you Monday.''

''Right,'' Brady murmured to the closing door. She sat where she was for quite a while, drinking the rest of her beer and staring at nothing. *You done good.*

She really hoped that was true.

"All rise."

Michael popped a peppermint into his mouth to help calm his stomach and slipped quietly into his chair. As he adjusted his robes, he let his glance travel around the room, searching.

Yes, she was there. In her usual place, but alone today, which was unusual. She was wearing something that looked a little like a Navajo horse blanket, and there was a yellow plastic butterfly keeping the hair out of her eyes. Her eyes seemed very large and even more intense than usual. Eyes a man could easily get lost in.

It was unexpectedly distracting, having her there. But what was even more unexpected was that it was also a comfort. Seeing her gave him an odd little lift in the region of his heart.

When all this is over, he told himself, I'll invite her to lunch. Maybe I'll ask her to have dinner with me. Maybe we can start at the beginning, square one. Get to know each other. Find out if we have anything at all in common.

He found himself hoping that they would.

It was lunchtime, and the courthouse mall was a busy place. People walked briskly along its broad pathways or strolled idly, killing the hour among the flowers and fountains. People sat alone on benches, eating lunches from brown paper bags, or moved about in gregarious groups, joking and laughing. One young woman wearing a bright yellow clip in her hair appeared to be waiting for someone; she would walk a short distance, check her watch, then retrace her steps. A few minutes later she would walk off in another direction and do the same thing.

From a vantage point on the roof of the courthouse, the assassin followed the yellow clip with the cross hairs of a telescopic sight. It would be a clear shot, an easy shot.

And pointless. There was something that had to be taken care of first. The picture, the drawing. It had to be found and destroyed. And after that . . .

The assassin lowered the rifle and moved from the shadows into the sunshine. It was a beautiful day. The air had the quality of a Mediterranean spring.

A shadow flicked across the sun. The assassin's reflexes jerked, then relaxed. It was only a hawk. Incredible to think there was such a creature living and hunting in the heart of this forest of steel and concrete. Fascinated, the killer watched the hawk soar silently over the mall, hover, then suddenly plunge straight down into a flock of pigeons foraging for crumbs. It was over in an instant, too quick for the human eye. The hawk rose into the sky clutching its prey in its talons, flew to a building a block or two away and settled onto its rooftop. A few soft gray feathers sifted away on the breeze.

The assassin, feeling a sudden affinity for the hawk, thought, That is what I am: a predator, silently watching, waiting for the moment to strike.

Down below in the mall, the woman with the yellow clip in her hair was on the move. The killer's eyes followed her as she crossed the mall and entered the tunnel that led to the Music Center complex. The assassin's eyes narrowed slightly with tension until the woman reappeared, emerging from the stairway near the Ahmanson Theater. They shone with a gleam of satisfaction as the woman made her way to a café near the theater and took a seat at an outdoor table.

Smiling, the assassin picked up the rifle and once again centered the yellow hair clip in the cross hairs. Not as clear a shot, but it would do. It would do very nicely.

"Startling new development in Gianelli case. Film at eleven!"

After lunch, when Kyle still hadn't shown up, Brady decided she was too restless and edgy to sit in court all afternoon staring at Michael and worrying about tonight's six o'clock news broadcast. She walked down to the shopping mall at Seventh and Figueroa and spent several hours wandering in and out of stores, buying nothing.

"KXLA has learned that several attempts have been made on the life of the presiding judge in the conspiracy trial of reputed mobsters Frank and Alberto Gianelli. Kyle Horner will have the exclusive story on tonight's edition of the news."

At about five o'clock, Brady got in her car and drove out to the television station. On the way, she stopped at a taco stand and picked up two burritos and munched as she maneuvered the car through the heavy rush-hour traffic.

"Coming up on KXLA's News at Six. Kyle Horner tells us who's trying to kill Judge Snow—and why. We'll have that story for you, and more—right after these messages."

At the station, Brady waved to the security guard and pulled her Jeep into the parking space that still bore Sean Flynn's name. Slinging her handbag over her shoulder, she ran up the steps to the back door of the soundstage. The guard on duty smiled and said, "Evenin', Brady," as he opened the door for her.

Picking her way through the maze of cameras and cables, Brady crossed the darkened soundstage toward the set. Tina Carrillo, KXLA's anchorwoman, was just sliding into her place behind the news desk. The light intensified, the cameras moved in a little tighter, and the director's voice murmured, "Three, two, one, you're on."

"Good evening, everyone, I'm Tina Carrillo, and this is the Monday edition of *The News at Six*. Tonight's top story—the incredible developments in the trial of reputed mobsters Frank and Alberto Gianelli. KXLA has learned that attempts have been made on the life of the presiding judge in the case, Michael A. Snow. Now, with the story, live from the courthouse, here is Kyle Horner."

Suddenly Kyle was on the monitor, appearing against a spangled backdrop of city lights. He was wearing a trench coat with the collar turned up. A breeze lifted the hair away from his forehead.

"On this spot, at approximately six o'clock last Friday night, Judge Michael A. Snow and an innocent bystander were almost run down and killed by a speeding car."

The station manager joined Brady in the darkness behind the cameras. "Great stuff," he murmured, his eyes on the monitor. "Good lead."

"Police department spokesmen declined to comment on whether this or the previous attempts on Judge Snow's life were connected to the conspiracy trial of alleged crime bosses Frank and Alberto Gianelli. They said only that—and I quote—the investigation is continuing, end quote. This is Kyle Horner, KXLA News."

Tina's head and shoulders filled the screen, except for a small box in the upper right. "Thank you, Kyle. What we are going to show you now is a truly remarkable drawing made by an eyewitness to the hit-and-run attempt on Judge Snow's life." The small box expanded to fill the screen. "If you think you know, or have seen, the person in this drawing, please contact the police immediately. The suspect is presumed to be armed. Do not attempt to apprehend him yourself. The hit-and-run vehicle is a dark-colored late-model sedan, and..."

Beside Brady, the station manager expelled his breath in a gust and muttered, "Beautiful, beautiful. You did a fantastic job, Brady. Just fantastic."

"Thank you," Brady mumbled. "Get out of my way, please. I need to go throw up."

Brady was late arriving at the courthouse on Tuesday morning. As so often happened after a rain, a Santa Ana had blown up during the night, making Brady's sinuses burn and keeping her awake with its banging and howling. She had gotten out of bed feeling itchy and cross and full of nameless apprehensions. She was never at her best when the northeast winds were blowing, but today she felt like a blind person on roller skates, as if terrible disasters were hovering just beyond reach.

Brady felt disaster move closer when she walked into the courtroom and found it all but deserted. The bailiff was at her desk; two of the defense lawyers were standing near the door, talking quietly, obviously on their way out of the room. In the seats usually occupied by members of the press, only Jim Washburn from the *Times* remained, scribbling notes on a small tablet.

"Are we in recess?" Brady asked in a whisper, dropping into the seat next to him.

"You might say that," the reporter drawled without looking up. "Indefinitely."

"Indefinitely?" Brady's mouth felt like paper. "Why?"

The reporter gave a snort of humorless laughter. "You missed the circus this morning. In a nutshell, the defense has moved for a mistrial."

"Mistrial?" Brady whispered. Disaster loomed, massive and unavoidable.

"Yep." The *Times* reporter tucked his notebook into his jacket pocket. "You know, I've been covering the courthouse beat for a lot of years. I don't think I've ever seen a man as stone-cold mad as Mike Snow was this morning. I'll tell you this," he said as he got to his feet, "I wouldn't want to be the one who leaked that story to Kyle Horner." He paused to give her a shrewd look. "You wouldn't happen to know anything about that, would you?"

"Nope," Brady said. "Sorry."

"Don't suppose you know where Horner is either, right?"

"Not a clue."

"Right. Well, I'd make myself scarce for a while if I were in his shoes. See you around."

"Right," Brady murmured.

She didn't know how long she sat there, reeling from the impact of disaster. When she thought her legs would support her, she stood and walked over to the railing. She cleared her throat, and the bailiff looked up. "Is Judge Snow in chambers?" The bailiff shook her head. Brady whispered, "Thank you," and walked out of the courtroom.

Downstairs in the main lobby she consulted the directory and found Michael Snow's office number. She turned back to the elevators, then changed her mind and went instead to a pay phone. She looked up the courthouse number in the phone book and dialed with shaking hands.

"Judge Snow's office, please."

The switchboard operator said, "What was that again, please?"

Brady cleared her throat and repeated herself. The operator muttered, "Thank you."

After a short wait, a young male voice said, "Judge Snow's office."

Brady cleared her throat again. "Yes, is he in, please?"

"I'm sorry." The voice was pleasant but unequivocal. "The judge isn't in at the moment. Would you care to leave a message?"

"No," Brady whispered. "That's all right. Thanks."

She cradled the receiver and checked her watch. Nearly lunchtime. Where in the world was Kyle? She picked up the phone again, deposited another twenty cents and dialed the station. Nobody there had seen him or knew where he had gone. She stood for a long time holding the receiver in her hand and staring at nothing. She felt cold and sick, restless and shaky.

It's the wind, she thought. I hate this damn wind.

Finally, with a leaden heart, she got in her car and drove back to the station.

As she passed through the main entrance lobby, the security guard on duty there flagged her down. "Somebody here to see you, Brady."

"Oh? Who?"

"He's in your office. Told me he'd produce a court order if necessary, and I sure as hell believed him. Thought I'd better warn you. It's the judge, the one on the news last—"

Brady said, "Oh God." Adrenalin carried her through the doors, down the hall and across the newsroom, like a leaf borne on the crest of a flood. At the entrance to her tiny cubicle she halted, shaking.

Michael was sitting on the corner of her desk, looking down at the oblong piece of polished wood he was turning over in his hands—the one with the brass nameplate on it that said "Sean Flynn." He let the silence stretch and become brittle. When he finally spoke, his voice was calm, even conversational.

"I was just curious," he said without taking his eyes off the nameplate. He looked up, and Brady felt his gaze like a physical blow. "I just wanted to know if you had any idea at all what you've done."

Chapter 8

Brady whispered, "Michael." That was all; there was nothing else she could say.

And there was so much she wanted to say. *Michael, I'm sorry. I wanted to help you, not hurt you. The last thing I would ever want to do is hurt you.*

His face—she knew every line, every angle, every hollow. She could draw his face blindfolded. She wanted to touch his face with her hands, trace its harsh lines and planes with her fingers and feel them relax and soften with his smile. *Michael, I'm sorry.*

But he was so cold, so aloof; she could no more reach out to him than she could embrace Mount Rushmore. What made that hurt so much was that he was still *Michael*, her Michael, the man who had carried her piggyback and held her through her nightmares. For some reason, at this moment he was allowing her inside his shell. She could feel his anger and frustration. She could see inside him, clear down to where the pain was, the sense of isolation and betrayal.

She could have dealt with anger alone. She was used to anger, the Irish kind, like dynamite—unpredictable, noisy and quickly gone. She didn't know what to do with this icy control, this slow killing freeze. Pain washed through her, leaving her feeling stripped and numb. All she could do was stand there, exposed and vulnerable, unable to protect herself from the hard, cold words—words that stung like hailstones.

"Mediaphobia," Michael said, drawing the word out, syllable by syllable. "Isn't that what you accused me of? Interesting word, but I really don't think it applies to me. Phobia—that means an unreasonable fear or dread, I believe. It seems to me that my fear of the media is entirely reasonable and justifiable." He put the nameplate down and took some time to align it precisely with the edge of the desk. When he continued, his tone was light, conversational. "The defense has moved for a mistrial, did you know that?"

Brady murmured an affirmation. His eyes flicked at her, dispassionate as stones. His voice became softer, but no less chilling. "Now that puts me in something of a dilemma. If I declare a mistrial, Brady, it will mean that I have surrendered to intimidation. I will be sending a message to the Gianellis, and others like them, that justice can be held hostage by violence. I will put law and order at grave risk in this town; the whole system will become vulnerable to threats, strong-arm tactics, intimidation. Do you understand?"

He waited for her nod. Her neck felt as if she were wearing a collar of iron.

"On the other hand, if I don't declare a mistrial and the Gianellis are convicted, it will almost certainly be overturned somewhere down the line. What all this means, at the very least, is that a lot of people will have spent a great deal of time and money for nothing. At worst, well, I don't really want to think about it." He closed his eyes and scrubbed a hand over his face, then took a deep breath and moved his shoulders as if trying to shift a heavy load. When he looked at her again his eyes weren't like stones any longer; they were dark and eloquent with accusation. This time, when he spoke, his words weren't hailstones—they were cannonballs.

"You knew how I felt, both professionally and personally. I didn't have to tell you a thing. I could have let you believe that hit-and-run was an isolated incident. I trusted you. And you chose to betray my trust."

It was a ringing indictment; the silence resounded with its echo. To Brady it was the sound of something precious shattering into a thousand tiny pieces, something *she* had broken.

She had thought that nothing could hurt worse than losing her father. Now she knew she had been wrong. Sean's death had been cruel and unexpected, but there had been comfort in the memories of the good times, and of the special love they'd shared. But this—this was the loss of something that hadn't even had a chance to begin. All that was left was a poignant, elusive vision of what might have been. She had faced Sean's death with the knowledge that she had never taken him for granted, that she had loved and appreciated him every day of his life and that there was nothing she could have done to prolong his existence. He'd lived and died on his own terms. But this precious thing she had lost—she had destroyed it all by herself.

I didn't mean to! she wanted to cry. I thought I was doing the right thing. I made a mistake. I'm sorry.

But she knew it was too late. "Sorry" wasn't going to fix anything. So, without a word, she turned and walked away.

Michael sat like a stone and watched her go. He felt both restless and drained, full of seething, boiling rage, yet empty. He was angry with her, with himself, with fate—angrier than he'd ever been in his life, angrier than he'd thought he ever could be. He wanted to yell at somebody, throw something, hit someone, break something—anything to release the terrible frustration inside him. And yet, at the same time, he felt something very much like remorse.

Damn it, she'd betrayed him! He'd trusted her. All right, that had been *his* mistake, an error in judgment. But what she'd done was unforgivable; she deserved his anger. So why did he feel as though he'd just kicked someone who was already down?

He never wanted to have anything to do with the woman again. She'd slipped into his life somehow when he hadn't expected it. She was an irritant; she made him feel edgy and uncomfortable, as if he had sand in his shoes. So why was it that right now all he could see were those haunting eyes of hers, glassy with tears? Witch's eyes.

Well, it was too late now. The words had been said, and since this wasn't a courtroom they couldn't be stricken from the record. Miss Flynn, you are instructed to disregard the judge's last statements.

Feeling old, Michael got to his feet and walked out of Brady's office. Maybe it wasn't too late to catch her. Maybe she hadn't left the studio. And if he did manage to find her, what could he say? I'm sorry? How could he be sorry when he was still so full of anger and frustration that he hurt inside?

The security guard in the front lobby told him that Miss Flynn had just left. No, she hadn't said where she was going or when she would be back. And yes, she *had* seemed just a mite upset.

Michael stood on the steps of the studio, scowling into the wind. Damn her, anyway. Here he was with a free afternoon and nothing to do with it except worry about where she might have gone and what she was doing and whether she was all right.

When a young woman carrying a clipboard bumped into him on her way out of the building, he gave in to a sudden impulse and interrupted her apology with a question. She looked doubtful, then thoughtful.

"Well, there's the Elephant Bar—lots of us go there for lunch and stuff. And there's this really off-the-wall dance club called Vertigo."

"No," Michael said carefully. "I mean a *hangout*—someplace you might get together after a hard day."

"Well, there's always Maxie's down on Melrose. And there's this place on La Brea some of the guys like, but I don't know it—"

"The news people—the old-timers," Michael said, suddenly inspired. "A guy like Sean Flynn—where would he go?"

"Sean?" The girl brightened. "Sean sure could put it away! He liked Maxie's. And he used to spend some time at a place called Gilhooley's—that's downtown. A lot of newspaper people go there, I guess. Sean used to work at the *Times*, you know. Years and years ago. And there's this place called 'the press box'—small letters. Lot of reporters, sports writers and stuff. Sean was a big baseball fan. Hey, you looking for anything in particular? Or anybody?"

Michael cleared his throat and tried her name. "Brady Flynn."

"Oh." The girl shrugged, then smiled. "Well, if I were you I'd try the press box. Brady's kind of a baseball nut, too. And if she's not there, then maybe Gilhooley's. It's a little mellower, if you know what I mean."

Brady found Gilhooley's blessedly cool and dim after the relentless brilliance outside. Her eyes felt itchy and furry, like tennis balls. She blamed it on the Santa Anas, which always swept the basin clear of smog and then dragged in that awful dry heat from the desert. It was hard to say which was worse.

Anyway, there was something comforting about the unpretentious shabbiness of Gilhooley's. At this time of the afternoon it was practically deserted—just a couple of guys throwing darts, and the intermittent clack of balls from the poolroom in the back. Brady had no trouble picking out the figure sitting alone at the bar.

As she took a stool next to him, she nudged his arm, the one he was using to prop up his chin. "Where have you been?"

Kyle squinted at her. "Hi, Brady."

"I've been looking all over for you."

"Yeah? Why?"

"What have you been doing all day?"

"Talking," Kyle said morosely. "To the pigeons."

The bartender came over and put a glass of beer on the counter. "There you go, Brady. How ya been?"

"What's that?"

The bartender smiled. "Your usual. I'm way ahead of you."

"What's that?" Brady pointed at Kyle's glass.

"Whiskey."

"Irish?"

"What else?"

"I'll have one of those. *And* I'll keep this," she said firmly, rescuing the glass of beer before the bartender could reclaim it. The bartender raised his eyebrows.

Kyle muttered, "Since when did you start drinking boilermakers?"

"Hey," Brady said, "I can drink anybody here under the table."

"*Sean* could drink anybody under the table. *You* have a two-beer limit. You don't even like whiskey."

"So what? I'm not drinking it because I like it."

"Why are you drinking it?"

"Because," Brady said grimly, "I mean to get *drunk*."

Kyle groaned and said, "Brady..."

"Look, it's either that or I find a freeway overpass to jump off."

Kyle considered that. "Well, either one will do the job, I guess. Jumping's messy, but drinking's slow."

"This stuff is less painful," Brady said, picking up the glass of whiskey the bartender had just set in front of her. She tossed it down and presently managed to wheeze, "I think." She plunked the glass down on the bar and focused on the bartender. "Hit me again."

The bartender put both elbows on the bar and covered his face with his hands. His shoulders were shaking.

"Hey," Kyle said. "Come on, now."

Brady said, "Oh, damn it," and covered her eyes with her hand.

"What'sa matter? Tell me. Hey, I'm your old buddy Kyle."

Brady uncovered her eyes long enough to glare at him. "Yeah, old buddy—where were you this morning, hmm?"

"I told you—talking to some people."

"You said pigeons. Don't you know what's happened?"

In a monotone, Kyle recited, "Court's in recess; defense moved for a mistrial."

"*I* was going to say that," Brady said, glaring at him. She sighed and covered her eyes again.

"I guess you've seen His Honor, right?"

Brady reached for her beer and swallowed a gulp that burned all the way down her throat. "I've seen him," she whispered.

Kyle looked shrewd. "I'd say from the look on your face that the judge is not a happy man."

"Kyle, you know what? I think I really screwed things up."

"Babe," Kyle muttered darkly, "you don't know the half of it."

"I really thought it was the right thing to do, Kyle. I thought I was just helping nail that guy. I mean, it didn't have anything to do with the trial. Right?"

Kyle cleared his throat and shifted on his stool. Brady prompted heavily, "Right?"

"That's where we screwed up, babe; we didn't wait to make sure of that. And even if we had, it probably would have had the same effect on the trial. Hell, I don't know. Damn it, I *knew* I should have waited to talk to my sources."

With a feeling of dark foreboding, Brady asked, "So what did your sources have to say about all this?"

Kyle began to laugh silently. After a moment he turned around and leaned back against the bar, the better to focus on Brady. "The word on the streets," he said solemnly, "is that there's a new kid in town. Imported from the east—far, far east. Hired gun," he explained patiently when Brady just looked dense. "A real pro. Crack marksman. That's what they say."

"I don't understand. Are you saying there *is* a contract on Michael?"

Kyle coughed. "Sort of."

"I don't understand. If this hit man is so good, how come he missed?"

Kyle began to laugh again. "That's just it. He was supposed to."

"I don't understand."

"Why do you think they needed a crack shot? Look, let me tell you something—the easiest thing in the world to do is blow somebody away. That's a sad fact, but it's true. If the mob wanted the judge dead, there are fifty guys right outside who'd do it for the price of a bottle of cheap booze. They didn't want him dead—they just wanted him shot at. And they wanted it in the papers, on TV. That was our job. See, we did 'em a big favor, baby."

"Why?" Brady's mouth was dry, so she drank some more beer. "Why would they go to that kind of trouble just to— what were they trying to do?"

"Just what they did do—with our help. Bust up that trial. The Gianellis were looking at a sure conviction. This way, they either get a mistrial or grounds for an appeal. However it turns out, it'll be a long, long time before they go to jail, and who knows what can happen in the meantime, huh?'' Kyle tapped his temple. "Smart. The trouble was the judge was keepin' it under his hat, so it wasn't working. Until we came along.'' He turned back to the bar and picked up his glass. "So, that's why I'm here. Cheers.''

"Is it helping?''

"Nope.''

"That's what I thought.'' Brady got up very slowly and waved at the bartender.

"Where you going?'' Kyle asked.

Brady shouldered her purse. "To find me an overpass.''

"Come on, Brady; it can't be that bad. We really thought we were doing a good thing. We just made a little mistake in judgment, that's all. He'll get over it.''

Brady shook her head. "I don't think so. See, I committed a . . . an unfidel—'' She stopped, frowning over the unexpected complexity of the word. "It's like I betrayed him,'' she said at last. "You know, like bein' infid—unfaithful.''

"Come on,'' Kyle said. "You mean that you two—''

Brady shook her head more emphatically. "*No.* It's worse than that. Michael is a very private person, and I betrayed his privacy. To a man like Michael, that's the ultimate, um, *infidelity.* Understand?''

After a moment Kyle murmured, "Sorry, Brady.''

Brady just nodded bleakly and pushed open the door.

Outside, it was just coming on dusk. The sidewalks were crowded, and the streets noisy with rush-hour traffic. The wind had died down a bit, but the air still felt hot and dry. Brady's head felt like a basketball, and the alcohol hadn't helped the awful sick feeling in her stomach at all.

The light at the corner had just changed to Don't Walk, but pedestrians were still pouring across the street. Brady joined them, not really knowing where she was going. Not really caring. On the way across the street, she thought she heard somebody call her name, but she didn't stop. It could only be Kyle, and she didn't feel like talking to him any more right now. She didn't feel like talking to anyone. She just wanted to walk until she fell off the edge of the world.

She didn't realize where she was going until she found herself in the courthouse mall. She didn't know what she was doing there. The building was closed, and Michael probably wouldn't be there anyway. Everyone was going home, moving purposefully, glad the day was over. Everyone but her. She was glad this dreadful day was over, but she had no purpose, and she didn't care if she ever went home.

The ultimate infidelity.

It seemed quieter near the fountain; the noise of the water shut out the din of traffic. With a sigh, Brady closed her eyes and let the moisture-cooled breeze soothe her aching head.

Something struck her hard, square in the middle of her back. She felt herself pitching forward, and even as her mind was rejecting what had happened, she instinctively threw out her arms to break her fall. Something tugged at her arm, wrenching it. The edge of the fountain slammed against her legs. She opened her mouth and managed to emit one small cry before the water rushed in to choke it off.

Michael was fifty yards or so from her—too far away to prevent what happened, though he saw it clearly, almost as if it were taking place in slow motion. He saw the slender figure in ragged denim—one of the city's horde of young, anonymous hoodlums—move in on Brady like a cruising shark. He saw the vicious blow, saw Brady lurch forward, hit the edge of the fountain and tumble over into the water.

All he could do was shout and break into a dead run. The assailant threw him a quick measuring glance, leaving him with a brief impression of a dark face beneath a knit cap as the thief stuffed Brady's purse inside his denim jacket. Then he was gone, dodging through the stream of pedestrians and disappearing into the Music Center tunnel. Michael didn't even try to give chase; the kid was already out of sight. And Brady was still face down in the water.

He wasn't the first one to reach her. By the time he'd vaulted over the side of the fountain and waded to where she was, some passersby already had her sitting up. She was coughing and gasping, very much alive. When she saw Michael she groaned, "Oh, no," and tried to flop over backward.

"Brady," Michael said, and was shocked at the way his voice sounded. "Are you all right?" She looked both comical and pathetic, like a half-drowned cat. Her hair was plastered to her face, her sweater was clinging to her body, and she'd lost her yellow butterfly clip.

"No," she said, and coughed some more. "Go away."

"Are you hurt?"

"I don't know. No. Just go away, please."

Michael nodded to the soaked good Samaritans who were still kneeling in the water beside her. "Thanks, I'll take it from here. I'm a friend of hers." He leaned over, put his hands under her arms and hauled her to her feet. When her knees buckled, he shifted one of his arms to the back of her legs and lifted her, dripping, into his arms. Her body was shaking, but he couldn't be certain how much of the trembling was due to her and how much was him.

"It's all over, folks," he said to the crowd that had inevitably gathered. "She's okay—just upset. Go on home now." To Brady he growled, "Put your arms around my neck, damn it!" He began to stride through the fountain, scowling against the spray. She drew in a long, quivering breath and lifted her hands to his neck. They felt cold.

A deputy sheriff, one of the courthouse contingent, came running up. He was joined a moment later by two uniformed members of the LAPD. Brady groaned and turned her face into Michael's shoulder. He silently echoed her dismay; all they needed now was a battery of reporters. They'd make the news two nights running.

"Can you stand up now?" he asked her. When she nodded, he sat on the edge of the fountain and swung his legs around to dry ground. One of the officers came to give him a hand, while the other one started to clear away lingering spectators. But Michael found that he had an odd reluctance to let go of Brady. She'd wrapped her arms around his neck and buried her face in the front of his sopping-wet shirt, so he shook his head at the police officer and for a few minutes just sat and held her in his lap, while his own breathing gradually quieted. When the hard, heavy thumping in his chest had eased a little, he lowered her feet gently to the ground, but he kept his arm around her waist while he gave the cop a quick account of the incident.

When he got to the part about her purse, Brady straightened as if she'd been jabbed in the ribs and put her hand over her mouth. "My purse," she said in outraged tones. "That jerk stole my purse!" She glared up at Michael and demanded, "Put me down!"

"Brady," Michael said gently, "you *are* down."

She looked down at her feet and muttered, "Oh."

Michael gave her a look filled with dawning suspicion. "Uh, look," he said to the cop, "can this wait till tomorrow? I think this young lady needs to get warm and dry as soon as possible." He reached inside his jacket and pulled out his wallet. "I'll make sure she gets down to file a report first thing in the morning, but right now I think I'd better see that she gets home."

The deputy came running up as the officer was peering at Michael's ID. "Judge Snow, Your Honor, I'm sorry, I didn't recognize you. Anything I can do?"

The officer glanced at him, looked at Michael and handed back his wallet. "I'm sure that'll be fine, Your Honor. Look, can we give you a lift?"

Michael glanced down at Brady. She was staring at him with wide eyes and an open mouth. Droplets of water quivered on the tips of her eyelashes. "Yeah, that'd be great."

"Where to, sir?"

Still looking at Brady, Michael replied with a grim smile, "My place—it's close by. This lady happens to be a friend of mine who lives out of town. I don't think she's in any condition to drive." The lady's mouth snapped shut.

"Squad car's right this way, sir. Can I give you a hand?"

"No, thanks, I've got her," Michael muttered as he lifted Brady into his arms again.

She gave a little sigh and put her arms around his neck without being told. Leaning close to his ear, she asked in a loud whisper, "Why do you keep carrying me?"

He laughed dryly and shifted her weight; the sibilance in his ear had sent a shock wave rippling down his spine. "Because I think it's probably easier than trying to get you to walk a straight line. How much have you had to drink?"

She drew back to peer at him with offended dignity. "Why do you ask?"

"Brady, for God's sake. Are you drunk?"

"Of course not," she said with a derisive snort. "I'm Irish. I'll have you know my father can drink anybody in this town under the table."

"Right, but what about you? How much did *you* drink?"

"I had one beer—"

"Come on, Brady."

"—At Maxie's, and one at the press box, and then I had a boilermaker at Gilhooley's. I was looking for Kyle," she explained in a stage whisper, sending another blast of shivers through his body.

"And that's all?" He was beginning to wonder if he was going to make it to the patrol car. An odd weakness seemed to be permeating his arm muscles.

"Yep." She made a cross on her chest. "Scout's honor." She frowned suddenly. "I prob'ly shouldn't've had the boilermaker. I have a two-beer limit, you know."

Michael breathed, "Oh, Lord." It was a prayer, not an oath.

"Here," the cop said sympathetically. "Wrap this blanket around her. It'll soak up some of the water."

Brady was very quiet on the way to Michael's temporary living quarters, which were located in a high rise near Bunker Hill. She sat in one corner of the squad car, as far away from Michael as she could get, and stared out the window. Every so often a shudder would ripple through her. Once in a while she'd sniff.

Michael sat in his own corner, conscious of her with every nerve in his body, but incapable of touching her. He was cold and wet, too, and furious with both himself and her. He couldn't understand himself anymore, and he sure as hell didn't understand *her*. He had to be out of his mind, taking her home with him, but what else could he do? He couldn't very well put her in her Jeep and leave her to drive herself all the way out to that godforsaken canyon of hers. But what in heaven's name was he going to do with her once he got her to his apartment?

The cops gave them an escort to the door. Michael thanked them; promising to see Lieutenant Sanchez first thing in the morning. They waved goodbye and left. Michael unlocked the door and pushed it open, and Brady went slowly inside, trailing the blanket behind her. When he had pushed the door closed she turned to look at him, then softly cleared her throat and rubbed her nose with a corner of the blanket. He stood still, jingling his keys and frowning back at her.

"Well," he said finally, tossing the keys onto a table, "I guess the first thing to do is get you out of those wet clothes."

She nodded. Her breath seemed to catch. A smile threatened, but was controlled when the tips of her small white teeth captured her lower lip.

"The bathroom's over there—through the bedroom."

She just went on standing there, looking at him. Dear God, he thought, how drunk is she, anyway? How drunk could a person be on three beers and a shot of whiskey? He wondered if she'd eaten anything today. He wondered if she might be in shock. He wondered if she'd hit her head on her way into the fountain. He wondered whether he ought to call a doctor. He wondered if he was losing his mind.

He didn't often find himself in a situation he couldn't handle, but at this moment he felt completely helpless.

In exasperation, he went to her and put his hands on her shoulders. Her eyes widened.

"Michael," she said, sounding surprised, "you look awful. You're all wet!"

He was so relieved to hear her voice that he burst out laughing. "Yeah, well, I guess we both went for an unexpected swim."

"That's right," she said slowly. "You were there." Her eyes narrowed. "Were you following me?"

"As a matter of fact," Michael said, "I was."

"Why?"

"I don't know. I was worried about you."

She turned her back to him. He saw the angle of her head change to one of stubborn pride. "You don't have to be. I'm just fine. I can take care of myself."

"Yeah," Michael said dryly. "I can see that. So do you want to start by getting yourself into the shower?"

The look she threw him over her shoulder made his heart give an unexpected bump. "What about you? Are you going to take a shower, too?"

"Eventually. I only have one bathroom,"

She drew herself up and said stiffly, "Then you go first. I don't want to put you out."

"Brady, get in the damn shower, or I swear I'll put you there myself!"

Oddly, his outburst of temper seemed to put her in a different mood altogether. She fought back a breathy giggle and murmured, "You wouldn't do that."

"Don't bet on it," Michael warned darkly.

"You wouldn't," she said blithely as she turned to stroll into his bedroom, "'cause you're an old fuddy-duddy."

Michael stood where he was, absolutely still. *Fuddy-duddy?* Oddly, he felt no inclination to laugh. "What do you—" he said, starting after her, but the bathroom door had closed. In a moment he heard the sound of the shower. He stared at the bathroom door while his mind repeated incredulously, Fuddy-duddy?

After a while, remembering how uncomfortable he was, he went into his bedroom and began to strip off his wet clothes. He did so with angry, jerky movements, without much regard for seams and buttons, which wasn't like him. He left them where they fell, which wasn't like him, either. He was just putting on his bathrobe when the bathroom door opened and Brady came out. She brought the tropics with her into his bedroom—steamy, torrid and heavy.

She was wearing a towel. Her hair was a rampant mass of curls, gilded by the lights as if by a tropical sun, her skin flawless matte velvet, as dewy and fresh as rose petals in the rain.

Michael's heart began to beat with a slow, drumlike cadence. He stared at her, entranced, watching the tips of her even white teeth press delicately into the soft, lush pillow of her lower lip.

"I need something to put on," she said. Her voice was low and husky.

Michael said, "uh," and reached blindly for a drawer. He took out a pair of pajamas and held them out to her. "Here, you can wear these."

"Oh…" Her laughter was low and husky, too. "Are these yours? Do you wear jammies to bed?"

"Only the bottoms," Michael muttered.

"Then I'll save them for you. I'll just wear the tops." Giving him a smile full of mischief and promise, she reached out to take the pajamas from his hands.

That was when Michael saw the bruises.

Chapter 9

They looked like stains left by dirty fingers. His fingers. The shock of seeing them there on the smooth satin skin of her arms was like a blow to the stomach. He felt sick, and there was a rushing sound in his head, as if an icy wind was blowing through it.

His hand shot out to catch her wrist; he pulled her toward him, turning her to the light. From a great distance he heard her say, "If you think those are pretty, you oughta see the one on my hip."

He blinked her face into focus. "Your hip?"

"Yeah, that's where I landed. It's bigger than a grapefruit; wanna see it?" Her eyes were cloudless skies; they seemed to go on forever.

"I'll take your word for it," Michael said roughly. "Go put something on." He gave her a little push and dropped her wrist. As she turned back into the bathroom, he thought he heard her mutter teasingly under her breath, "Chicken."

When the door had closed on her throaty chuckle, he shut his eyes and concentrated on breathing slowly and deeply.

She had a way, it seemed, of fogging up his vision and making it hard for him to focus on what was right or who he was. She filled his mind with sensual images of soft lips and moist, heated skin. She made him burn with desires he'd almost forgotten about and think things he had no business thinking. Not now. And not about her.

He thought, Dear God, what have I done to her? In his mind he saw again the ugly marks on her fragile skin, and that vision scattered the earlier erotic images like so many dry leaves. He had no right to blame her for anything; she hadn't asked for this. She'd been happy before the blight on his life had spread to hers, infecting her like a virus. She was a victim of his troubles, not the cause of them. He could not—must not—let her be hurt any more. Least of all by him.

Warm protective feelings slowly filled him, but most of them evaporated the moment she walked out of his bathroom wearing his pajama top and absolutely nothing else. Because before he had a chance to rally his defenses, she put her hand on his cheek, stood on tiptoe and kissed him full on the mouth.

In a way, it was an innocent kiss—generous, uninhibited, unequivocal. But when she spoke there was nothing innocent about her voice; it was husky, sultry, with an intimate timbre that caressed his auditory nerves like knowing fingers.

"It's all right, you know. They don't hurt. I know you'd never hurt me."

His body was one silent groan; he ached with the strain of self-denial. He felt her hand on his face and wondered how long he was going to be able to keep from turning his mouth into the warm hollow of her palm. He closed his eyes and whispered, "Brady," and felt his lips touch hers as he said her name.

"Michael, I'm sorry." Her breath was the faintest of sighs.

"Sorry? Why?" His fingers were touching her chin so lightly, so gently, that he barely felt he was touching her at all.

"I'm so sorry I betrayed you. I never meant to hurt you. I only wanted—"

"I know. I know." It was his own body that was betraying him now, his hand that moved of its own volition, applying the slightest pressure on her chin. She responded to that unspoken request and opened her mouth; he groaned softly and covered it with his, claiming it as his, possessing it.

She was so open, so giving, as wanton and unrestrained as a summer wind; his need was a spark, stirred to conflagration by the wind's passing. Whatever it was that had begun that stormy night when he'd first kissed her, it had been steadily growing, until now it was something he couldn't control. He couldn't get enough of her mouth, couldn't penetrate deeply enough to satisfy him. With his lips and tongue he explored it thoroughly, inside and out, and he still wanted more.

He slipped his arms under the pajama top and dragged her hard against him, feeling her heart knock against his chest, marveling at the suppleness of her naked body, the subtlety of her curves. Rejoicing, he felt her respond to his touch, felt her body slide sinuously against him with an instinctive seeking. He heard the sound she made, a little feminine growl of pleasure at the evidence of his desire.

He could take her now, right here; his robe was a scant barrier, and her pajama top none at all. All it would take...

The thought slashed through his consciousness with graphic clarity, shocking him so badly that he pulled away from her. With all his muscles quivering in protest, he stared down into her dazed blue eyes and uttered one strangled syllable. *"No."*

Brady licked her swollen lips, and he followed the movement of her tongue the way a starving man gazes at forbidden fruit. She touched his mouth with her fingertips and whispered, "What's wrong?"

Gently he pulled her hand away from his face and held it against his chest. "This is wrong."

"Why?"

His laugh was painful. "For heaven's sake, Brady, you're—you've had too much to drink."

Her lower lip quivered and threatened to escape the discipline of her little white teeth. She gazed up at him and murmured, "Only a tiny bit." Her hand slipped inside the front of his robe. "Saint Michael, do you *always* have to do what's right?"

"It doesn't take a saint to know that—*Brady*." She had leaned over to nuzzle inside the deep slash of his bathrobe. His hands tightened convulsively on her shoulders. "Brady, do you know what you're doing to me?"

She nodded. "Uh-huh." Her lips were making soft, moist tracks down his chest.

"I ought to turn you over my knee." His voice felt hollow; it definitely lacked conviction.

Brady's laugh blew warmly on his skin. "Feel free. Just remember what I'm wearing under this pajama top."

His groan was raw frustration. Gripping her arms hard enough to add to her set of bruises, he held her away from him. "Damn it, Brady! What do you think you're doing? I'm not a *saint*. I just have to be able to live with myself, that's all. Why are you so determined to make it hard for me?"

"Why do you keep treating me like a child?"

"Because you're acting like one!"

"Oh, no," she said softly, smiling. "I'm not—and that's what's making it hard for you, isn't it? I'm sorry, Michael. I'm not going to let you put a generation gap between us."

He glared at her, furious with himself, furious with her, and as confused as he'd ever been in his life. When he uttered an inarticulate sound and turned away from her to-

ward the bathroom, she gave another of those husky laughs
that seemed to go straight to his loins.

"Cold shower, Michael?"

He straightened his shoulders, getting a firm grip on his
dignity and self-control. Dropping his eyelids, he said aus-
terely, "I suggest you go out to the kitchen and find yourself something to eat. That might help you sober up a little.
I think there's some milk in the refrigerator."

"Oh, good," Brady said. "Can I have cookies, too?"

Michael gave her a long quelling look, which she returned with wide-eyed innocence. Finally, feeling a traitor-
ous bubble of laughter forming inside his own chest, he
growled, *"Brat!"* and closed the bathroom door.

A shower and a shave helped to restore his natural
aplomb, so when he came out of the bathroom to find Brady
occupying his bed he felt nothing more than a mild thump
in his midsection. He was entirely capable of dealing with it;
he'd known his apartment had only one bed before he'd
made the decision to bring her here. And if the sight of her
hair on his pillows made his hands tingle with the urge to
touch it, so what? He was a mature, responsible man, not
an adolescent with overactive glands.

He just hoped and prayed she was already asleep.

His prayer was not to be answered. When she heard the
bathroom door open she lifted her head from the pillows
and, propping it on one hand, regarded him from under a
sweep of tawny lashes. She gave him a smile of surpassing
sweetness, but Michael wasn't fooled; to him she had the
deceptively somnolent look of a sleepy lioness.

"You took so long, I got sleepy." Her voice still had a
husky rasp. "I hope you don't mind."

Michael cleared his throat. "No, not at all. Go right
ahead."

She yawned. "I know it's early. I don't know why I'm so
tired."

"Alcohol and adrenaline," Michael muttered.

"Hmm?"

"Never mind."

Brady settled back, pillowing her head on her arm. Her cheeks looked flushed, warm, soft. "Michael?"

"Yes?"

"When are you coming to bed?"

He felt another thump in his midsection—a harder one this time. He blinked and said, "I beg your pardon?"

Her mouth softened and curved into a smile. "You only have one bed, Michael."

He coughed and said, "So I have."

"This is a very nice bed. Nice and comfortable." Michael found himself mesmerized by the snuggling movements her body was making underneath the covers. "I don't want to put you out of your bed. If you insist on being a fuddy-duddy about it, *I'll* sleep on the couch." A pair of incredibly long, shapely legs slipped out from under the blankets.

Remembering in the nick of time what she was wearing, Michael gasped, "No—no, you stay put. That's perfectly all right. The couch will be just fine."

"That's silly...." Her voice trailed away into another yawn. "I won't bite you, you know. And it's not like we've never slept together before, remember?"

He did, unfortunately; he remembered every detail of the way she'd felt in his arms, so clearly that for a second or two he couldn't speak. She took full advantage of his silence.

"If I promise to be good, will you sleep with me?"

His mind absolutely refused to behave itself. It jumped on that double entendre with the unabashed delight of a child meeting a rain puddle. And there was no way in the world to keep his appreciation from Brady; the gleam in his eyes and the reflexive twitch at the corners of his mouth betrayed him. Her answering giggle rippled through him like sparkling wine, making him feel absurdly lighthearted.

"Oops," she murmured, the contrition in her voice be-lied by the twinkle in her eyes. "I guess I just blew it, huh? I don't think you trust me."

"Brady," Michael said fervently, trying not to laugh, "I'd have to be either crazy or incapacitated to trust either one of us! Go to sleep, damn you." Moving quickly while he was still capable of mature and responsible action, he went out and closed the door.

When he reached the living room, he paused to breathe deeply and massage his neck muscles. His stomach growled, reminding him that it was long past the dinner hour, so he went in to the tiny kitchen. An empty milk glass and a box of crackers were sitting on the counter. Michael opened a can of minestrone and, while he waited for it to heat, ran water into the milky glass and munched a handful of the crackers.

When the soup was hot, he took it into the living room. Before he sat down to eat, he put a tape into his stereo system—the one personal luxury he'd brought with him into exile. After a few minutes he got up and turned it off; he found that he wasn't in the mood for Bach.

He turned on the television, and found an old Doris Day movie he hadn't seen in years. While he watched it, he stretched out on the couch, draping his feet over the edge. Long before the movie was over, he'd come to the conclu-sion that if God had intended him to sleep on couches he'd never have given him a six-foot-four-inch frame.

Thoroughly disgusted with himself, he got up and turned off the television. This was ridiculous. He had a perfectly good bed—a comfortable bed—right in the other room. It was occupied by a beautiful, sexy, desirable woman, but so what? She must be sound asleep by now, and surely he was mature and responsible enough to control his carnal urges.

Michael carried his soup bowl into the kitchen and ran water into it. Then he turned off the lights in the living room and slowly and cautiously opened his bedroom door. There was no sound from within except the sigh of deep, even breathing. Sending up a heartfelt prayer of gratitude, he tiptoed to the bed, slipped under the covers—and made two unfortunate discoveries.

The first discovery was that, though the bed was plenty big enough for two, Brady was occupying the middle of it. The second was that she was a very light sleeper. He had barely settled onto the mattress when he heard the tempo of her breathing alter. She murmured something sleepy and inarticulate and moved to him as if his body had a gravitational pull on hers. She fitted herself to him as if they were still occupying her narrow couch instead of a king-size bed.

"Michael?" Her hand roved over his chest, found a pectoral muscle and seemed to like the way it conformed to the curve of her palm. "I'm glad you're here."

Michael captured her wandering hand and, because he didn't know what else to do with it, brought it to his mouth and pressed a kiss into the warm palm. "Hush," he said gruffly. "Go back to sleep."

"Michael?" Her head moved against his shoulder; her words blew shivers into his ear. "I'm sorry I called you an old fuddy-duddy. I didn't mean it—not like *old*."

"That's a relief," Michael muttered.

"I meant dignified." She sighed and moved sinuously against him. "You're so damn dignified, that's the trouble."

"You obviously didn't see me hurl myself fully clothed into a public fountain this evening," he said dryly. Nor was she reading his thoughts at this very moment, thank God.

"Why do you always have to be—" She dropped her voice an octave and intoned, "The Honorable Michael A. Snow? By the way, what does the *A* stand for? Allen? Aloysius?"

"Aaron."

"Aaron? Hmm, nice." She gave another little wiggle.

"Glad you like it." His voice had become ragged.

"The Honorable Michael Aaron Snow. *Honorable*. You really take that seriously, don't you?"

"I try." And never, he thought, had he been so sorely tried; he was so tense that his body felt like one giant charley horse. "Lately you've been making it very hard for me."

"Have I?" He could almost hear her purr. "Good, because I want you to come down off Mount Rushmore and just be Michael for a while. I really like Michael."

Mount Rushmore? Dear Lord, was that how she thought of him? Didn't she know what she was doing to him? He'd never felt less like a monument in his life—except for his jaw, which was clenched so tightly that it felt as if it had turned to stone. His body was an inferno, his mind a cauldron. Right this minute he was half-crazy with wanting her, with wanting to roll her under him, wrap her long, slender legs around him and bury himself in her. He wanted to forget about restraint and control. He was tired of being stretched to the breaking point. He wanted to let go, let control snap, let passion take him. He wanted to take her quickly, savagely, and then, with the edge off his hunger, make slow, exquisite love to her, to every part of her, in every way he'd ever heard of, all night long....

So what was stopping him? He wasn't a saint. To the best of his recollection, he'd taken no vows of chastity. The woman sharing his bed—and his pajamas—was a consenting adult. Why was he torturing himself like this?

But he'd already been through all the arguments during that unbelievable weekend he'd spent with her at her place. That weekend seemed only a misty memory now, like a dream trip to never-never land. He'd wrestled with his code of ethics and with the natural wariness learned from past mistakes, and nothing had happened to change the way he felt. Still, he might have been able to overcome his reservations if something even more insurmountable hadn't gotten in his way.

Because, although he wanted her so badly it was killing him, in some way he didn't entirely understand he felt *protective* of her. He knew he was responsible for putting her at risk, and somehow he knew he was capable of doing her terrible damage. And though she was putting him through some of the worst moments of his life, it was infinitely better than trying to live with himself if he let her get hurt.

He must have made some sort of sound that betrayed his frustration, because Brady suddenly touched his mouth with her fingertips, then laid her hand on his cheek. It was a curiously tender caress, and so unexpected it made his throat ache.

"I'm sorry, Michael." Her voice had a catch in it, too. "I'm sorry. I didn't mean to tease you. I don't know what's the matter with me."

"Brady, it's all right. You'll feel better in the morning." Now he worried that she was close to tears. He didn't know what might happen if he tried to comfort her. "Please, just try to go to sleep."

She sniffed and whispered, "All right," and turned on her side, facing away from him but still touching all along the length of his body. Her voice was muffled, groggy. "I know what you think. You think I'm a prom–promiscuous brat."

"I don't—"

"You know something? You prob'ly won't b'lieve this, but I'm practic'ly a virgin."

With that absurdity she was finally, blessedly, obliviously asleep.

Michael lay very still, a bubble of ironic laughter tormenting him like an incipient sneeze. *Practically a virgin?* She was good at throwing tantalizing remarks at him and then leaving them unresolved. What was the other thing she'd said? Oh, yes, she'd compared him to Mount Rushmore.

Since it looked like a long night, and since there was no way in the world he was going to figure out what she'd meant by "practically a virgin," he thought about that, about Mount Rushmore. *Come down off the mountain, Michael.*

Somewhere in the bleak and lonely hours, with Brady's warm, firm bottom pressed against his hip, it came to Michael that he'd become very good at what he did—maintaining order and staying in control. He was good at making tough decisions, holding himself aloof from personal involvement, keeping his emotions inviolate—so good that it had become a habit he couldn't break. He didn't know when it had happened, but somewhere along the line he had become an impartial observer of his own life.

There is a time in every big city night when no one stirs but the mean, the hungry, the restless. Traffic lights blink at empty streets, and refuse blows unobstructed along the sidewalks. The wail of a siren echoes down the concrete canyons like the cry of a wolf.

Too restless and frustrated to sleep, the assassin paced, carefully avoiding the handbag and its contents strewn across the floor; avoiding, too, the drawing tablet that lay open on the bed, its pages in disarray. There was no point in looking through them anymore—the drawing wasn't there. It was gone, torn from the book.

The assassin fought to control a rising tide of rage. The drawing that had been on television was unimportant. It was featureless, anonymous, harmless. But the other one... In making that sketch, the artist had stolen pieces from her unsuspecting subject's soul. She had seen beyond the surface disguises. She would recognize, and remember.

The siren's wail drew the assassin to the window, but the cold lights of the deserted street held no surcease for the rage or the restlessness.

For the second time in her adult life, Brady woke with her cheek pillowed on a masculine chest. The chest was rising and falling steadily, but not deeply; half fearfully, she tilted her head and looked up into brooding indigo eyes.

"Good morning," Michael rumbled. "I trust you slept well?"

Memory returned with mortifying clarity. She closed her eyes and said huskily, "Oh, no."

His fingers ruffled her hair. "Come on, it's not that bad."

Did she only imagine the gentle amusement in his voice? She tilted her head, looking for the creases at the corners of his eyes, and accidentally brushed his lips with the tip of her nose. He obligingly formed them into the shape of a kiss. Her heart gave a little skip of wonder.

"It's bad enough," she muttered. "I remember it all, you know."

"Hmm. Are you sure? You were pretty drunk. You might have imagined things."

"I wasn't that drunk. Not nearly drunk enough. I don't even have a decent hangover." She lay back in the curve of his arm and was beginning a languorous stretch when something else occurred to her. She raised her head from Michael's shoulder, lifted the blankets, peered under them and groaned. "Oh, God, I remember that, too. I'm not wearing any bottoms."

"That's all right," Michael said placidly. "I am."

"I practically *attacked* you."

"I seem to have survived."

She hadn't imagined it. There was gentleness, even tenderness, in his voice. As she listened she became aware that his body was a furnace lying all along the length of hers, and that her hand was on his naked chest. Her fingers were burrowing through the thicket of hair, exploring textures, seeking the heat, and his heartbeat was surging beneath her hand like a wild thing. And he was making no move to restrain her.

Awed, she raised herself on one elbow in order to look at his face. His mouth—his beautiful poet's mouth. She'd never seen it so relaxed, so sexy, so incredibly inviting. But she was sober now, stone-cold sober, and she'd made enough of a fool of herself with this man to last her a life-time. Licking her lips, she moved her gaze upward, search-ing for his eyes. The look she found in them stopped her heart for a beat or two, then kicked it into a new and pain-ful rhythm. She listened to it for a moment, then whis-pered, "This doesn't seem right."

"What doesn't?"

"This. Being here with you, like this. Like we've…when we haven't."

He didn't answer. His silence and his heat folded in on her, suffocating her; her body felt swollen and tight. It hurt to draw air into her lungs, to swallow. Her heartbeat hurt. It hurt to *be*.

No. It hurt to be with *him*. To be *with* him, but *not* with him.

To be touching him with the entire length of her body, to have his hipbone pressing against the juncture of her thighs and her breast against his rib cage, was exquisite plea-sure—and intense pain.

She wanted to touch him with her hands and her mouth, tenderly and with joy.

She wanted to love him. She did love him.

And that *hurt*.

Quickly, before he could feel the pain shuddering inside her, she rolled away from him, sliding to the far side of the bed. She sat up, reaching for the floor with her bare feet, tugging at the pajama top to make sure it was going to cover her bottom when she stood up.

"Brady, wait." He reached across the wide expanse of tumbled bedclothes and caught her arm. "Don't go."

She jerked her head angrily around to stare at him. "Why not?"

The grip on her arm eased. His fingers began to move slowly up and down on the pajama sleeve, right over the place where the bruises were. She heard the soft expulsion of his breath. "Brady, look, please don't feel embarrassed."

"Why not? I made a complete idiot of myself, didn't I?" And she was going to again. She felt herself shiver.

"No—no, you didn't." She felt his hands on her shoulders, felt his solid presence there at her back. And with all her being she *hurt.* "Brady, believe me, you have no idea how hard it was for me to keep from—"

She jerked away from him and turned to face him. "Then why did you?"

"Damn it, you were drunk!"

"Not *that* drunk!"

"Yeah? Well, tell me—how drunk do you have to be to qualify? Am I supposed to administer a breath test? Damn it, Brady, I have a set of rules that I live by, and those rules say a man doesn't take advantage of a woman who's had too much to drink!"

"Yeah? Well, if you ask me, it makes a pretty convenient excuse. I bet if you try you can just keep right on coming up with reasons not to 'take advantage'—like don't take advantage of a woman who's been caught in the rain, or a woman who's having a nightmare! *Never* take advantage of a woman under forty, because she's probably too young and stupid to know what she wants! And for heaven's sake never take advantage of a woman who's *crying*!"

She was on her feet, facing him with fists clenched, the skimpiness of her clothing forgotten. It was her temper, of course, which wasn't surprising—she was long overdue. The incredible thing was that suddenly Michael seemed to be as angry as she was. He sat on the edge of the bed with his fists resting like chunks of rock on his thighs. His chest heaved, and his eyes smoldered. He bore a closer resemblance to Mount Saint Helens than to Mount Rushmore.

"Brady," he growled, "knock it off."

Brady knew a surge of unreasoning exultation. She was cracking his armor, making him angry, making him lose control! She wasn't afraid of his anger—not this kind of anger. This she could understand. This she could combat on her own terms.

"Oh, how about this one?" she taunted. "Don't take advantage of a woman's friendship. Or her vulnerability. And the cardinal sin: don't take advantage of a woman who's stupid enough to fall in lo—"

"That's *enough*!" He was on his feet now, too, gripping her arms, shaking her. "What the hell do you think I'm made of? Stone? Do you have any idea what you put me through last night? While you were sleeping it off with your bare bottom tucked against my middle, what do you suppose I was doing? Huh? What do you think I went through last weekend, trying to keep—" He broke off in midsentence, staring at her. He made a sound, a muttered oath, and, catching a handful of her hair, pulled her head back. His mouth caught her startled gasp and smothered it.

It happened so quickly. She was shocked, unprepared. Whatever she'd hoped to goad him into, she hadn't expected this. She was overwhelmed, she couldn't breathe. Panic whimpered silently inside her chest. With a perversity born of fear, she fought him.

And because she fought him, he had to subdue her. His hand tightened in her hair; his tongue ravaged her mouth and possessed it. His arm caught her around the waist and lifted her hard against him while his body arched above hers, bearing her back and down.

The struggle was brief. The shock waves of panic rippled through her and then receded, leaving her weak and shaky. Her knees buckled, and she clung to his arms, his shoulders, his neck. She felt herself being lifted and settled into his lap. The fingers tangled in her hair relaxed, and began to move slowly, sensuously, over her scalp. Her neck muscles melted, dropping her head back on the rigid pillow of his arm. When he gentled the kiss, allowing her to tear her mouth free, her first breath was a ragged cry, *"Michael..."*

His reply was an inarticulate murmur as his lips and tongue began a gentler subjugation, caressing her mouth with warm liquid strokes that left her trembling. The hand that supported her lower body moved slowly downward over the swell of her hip and along the back of her thigh; her body moved in unconscious response, curling inward, toward his. Slowly his hand began the return journey, lightly brushing her skin, savoring its texture. It reached the bottom edge of the pajama top and continued upward, pushing away the barrier that separated their heated bodies.

Brady drew in air when her belly touched his. His textures intrigued and delighted her: the soft, crisp tickle of hair, the satiny warmth of skin. Her breasts, still hidden under folds of fabric, swelled and tightened; the chafing of cloth on their tender tips became intolerable. She made a soft sound of feminine need and tore her mouth from his, arching her head back, offering, inviting.

He took what she offered, closing his mouth over the vulnerable curve of her throat, dragging the edges of his teeth lightly along the cords of her neck, tracing the line of her collarbone with his tongue. And beneath the pajamas her breasts ached and yearned, wanting the touch of his mouth, his hands, the crushing weight of his chest.

She ignored the intrusive sound for a while; her mind simply refused to accept it. *No! No, not now, go away!* But it didn't go away. It came again, louder, more insistent. She drew a quick, shuddering breath and whispered, "Michael..."

But he had already heard it. His neck muscles had gone rigid beneath her hands. His breath sighed along her collar bone and made a warm pool in the hollow of her neck. After a moment he lifted his head. His eyes were closed, and

there were deep grooves etched in his cheeks. Brady put her
hands on his face, trying to smooth the lines of strain.

"Michael."

"I know," he said. "I heard it. Someone's knocking."

Chapter 10

Michael cursed with restrained savagery and raised his voice to call, "Who is it?"

"Police," an officious voice bluntly responded. A second voice softened that by adding diplomatically, "Sorry to bother you, Your Honor."

Swearing with an eloquence that made Brady gaze at him with new admiration, Michael rubbed a hand over his face, then began to shake with silent laughter. Brady recognized it as pure frustration, for which laughter was probably as good a safety valve as anything. She knew how he felt. She was beginning to shake herself, though not with laughter.

"Be right there," Michael shouted. The cops chorused obligingly, "Take your time."

With his hand still covering the lower part of his face, Michael looked down at her as if the sight hurt his eyes. "Well, it seems the world's still out there," he said dryly. "Reality to the rescue."

Brady found that she couldn't speak, so she just swallowed and cleared her throat. She'd already tugged the pajama top down as far as it would go. She found that dignity was hard to come by when you were lying half naked in a man's lap, but managed to achieve at least a modicum of it as she raised herself to a sitting position.

"Listen," Michael said harshly, "I'm sorry about this. This should never have—"

"Don't," Brady rasped, gratified to discover that her vocal cords were functioning, even if only on a fundamental level.

Michael just nodded grimly and eased her feet to the floor. She snatched at her meager covering and stood up, leaving him sitting there rubbing the back of his neck. After a moment he got up and reached for his bathrobe.

"Stay here and get dressed," he said softly. "I'll go let them in. Take as long as you need."

Brady watched him go and then sank down onto the bed. Her legs felt like noodles. For a few minutes she sat listening to the murmur of voices from the other room, fighting a powerful urge to burst into tears.

I don't believe this, she thought. I can't belive I've done this. Either I'm acting like a stupid teenager with a horrendous crush—or I'm really in love with him!

And the odds were it was love. She'd had crushes before, and they'd never hurt like this. The realization didn't make her feel better, but since there wasn't much she could do about it, she simply sniffed once and got resolutely to her feet.

When Michael came back into the room she was just buckling herself into his trench coat, cinching the belt tightly around her middle. He had his mouth open to say something, but when he saw her, he closed it abruptly.

"My clothes are a soggy mess," she muttered. "I hope you don't mind if I borrow this."

"Not at all." He cleared his throat delicately. "Dare I ask what you found to wear under it?"

"Don't worry," she said with an airy toss of her head that did little to ease the ache in her throat. "I'm not planning to flash anybody. What did the cops want?"

Frowning distractedly at her, he made an impatient gesture with his hand and muttered, "Oh, Lieutenant Sanchez wants to see you—us. I guess they've had a few responses to that telecast. He's sent a squad car to give us a lift to the station. I told them to wait downstairs. Brady..."

"Got a rubber band?" She had raked most of her hair into a ponytail and was holding on to it with one hand while she poked through the objects on his dresser top with the other.

He blinked and said, "What?"

"For my hair. I can't go to the police station looking like a sheepdog."

"Oh." Looking harassed, he stepped to the closet and began riffling through a rack of ties. "Here," he muttered, pulling out a black knit one. "Will this do?"

"Can I have that red one?"

He threw her a look, but reached for the red one. He started to hand it to her, then said gruffly instead, "Here, I'll do it. Tip your head down."

So Brady tucked in her chin and held on to her hair while Michael tied his necktie around it. "This is crazy," he muttered, dropping his hands but not moving away from her.

"What is?"

"This. Us, me. I can't—"

"One of us is crazy, that's for sure." She wanted to move away from him, but couldn't seem to get her legs to work. So instead she folded her arms across her body and tucked each hand into the opposite sleeve. Thus protected, she managed a harsh laugh. "I seem to be the one who's not playing with a full deck here."

"Why do you say that?"

"Why do I say that? My God, I've just spent an entire night making a complete fool of myself." She gave her head an angry shake and started to move away from him. He caught her arms and turned her to face him, then dropped his hands, as if touching her were painful.

"Brady, you haven't made a fool of yourself."

"Oh, yeah? I've fallen for George Washington. If that's not foolish, I don't know what is!"

"George Washington?" He looked so bewildered that Brady might have laughed—if she'd been in a laughing mood.

"Never mind," she muttered, fastening her gaze on the middle of his chest. "It wasn't funny."

"George Washington?" Michael repeated incredulously. He touched her chin, gently tilting it upward. She tried to resist him. "Is that what you think of me—even after this morning?"

She sniffed, and drawled sardonically, "Well, don't feel too bad about this morning. I imagine even old George had his breaking point."

He lifted his hands to grip her arms, but then let them drop to his sides. "Brady, it isn't that I didn't—don't—want to make love to you." He gave a harsh laugh. "That was pretty obvious. In my case, it's not something I can hide. But as long as I'm involved in this mess, I can't let myself get involved, don't you see? Not with anyone. I can't risk having someone else get hurt just because they're too close to me. You almost got killed because you tried to return a brief. My God, I'd never forgive myself if anything happened to you because of me. Do you understand?"

She looked up into his face, hating the strain and anguish she saw there, aching to ease it somehow but knowing that she couldn't. Knowing, too, that he was probably right. "Yes," she whispered. "I understand." She licked her lips. "And what about after, Michael? What happens when it's all over?"

There was a very long silence. Brady began to feel cold. Finally Michael let go of a breath and said softly, "God knows, I want you—I'd be crazy not to. You're a beautiful, sexy, desirable woman. There's all kinds of chemistry between us. But, damn it, Brady, four days ago I didn't even have your name right. And right now, as far as I can see, the only thing we've got in common is the fact that somebody tried to kill us. That's hardly something you can build a long-term relationship on!''

''Who's asking you for a long-term relationship?'' Her chin was up, and her eyes were narrowed in what her father would have called a "fightin' look.'' Her mouth twisted with an acidic little smile. "I'm a member of the Now Generation, remember? The ones born after the bomb? Hey, if something good comes along, we go for it. There might not be a tomorrow, right? Look, damn it, I don't need some kind of *commitment*.''

There was another silence, then another expelled breath. "That's just the point I'm trying to make, Brady—about the differences between us. Because, you see, I do.''

They stared hard at each other while Brady counted her heartbeats in a slow and painful cadence. Then she snapped, "Fine!'' and turned away. "Hey, listen, no big deal. Far be it from me to compromise your principles, Your Honor.'' She had to stop suddenly to swallow the quiver that was threatening to creep into her voice. Frowning distractedly at nothing, she said, "Um, do you have a spare toothbrush?''

Again Michael put out a hand to touch her, and again he let it drop. "I'll see,'' he said regretfully, and turned away.

The assassin, watching from a vantage point on one of the elevated walkways, saw the two people emerge from the apartment building and get into the squad car, and smiled. It was gratifying to be right about all those sketches the artist had made of the judge. Guessing that she had a thing about His Honor had made picking up her trail easier than expected. She had been easy to follow; she was so predictable. After her harrowing experience she had obviously spent the night being comforted by the judge, and right now she was on her way to the police station to file a report of her unfortunate mishap. And after that—home, of course, for a change of clothes.

The assassin took out a wallet, opened it to reveal the driver's license and smiled. The quarry, unsuspecting, was about to go to her lair—only to find the hunter waiting.

There would be plenty of time for a thorough search, and once that infernal drawing had been found and destroyed, the girl would be next.

The first thing Brady noticed about Lieutenant Sanchez was that he didn't look Hispanic. The second was that in spite of his crisp, buttoned-down appearance there was something about his eyes that made her certain he was another man Sean Flynn would have liked at his back in a fight.

He also had the tense, slightly harassed look of a man in a quandary. The way he regarded them as he sat perched on a corner of his desk reminded Brady of certain memorable childhood visits to the principal's office.

Michael wasn't one to be intimidated. Beating Snachez to the punch, he seated himself and bluntly asked, "Well? What have you got?"

Ignoring the question, Sanchez matched him stare for stare for a few moments, then abruptly shifted his gaze to Brady. "Filed your report okay?"

Brady nodded. She'd taken care of the red tape involved in reporting her purse-snatching while Sanchez had been busy in interrogation.

"Good. In a few minutes I'm gonna find you an empty desk, and I want you to look at some pictures, okay? I may want to put together a lineup for you a little bit later on. Any problem with that?"

The inquiry was polite, velvet on steel. Brady shook her head. Sanchez nodded. "Good. Before we do that, though,

I'd like you to take a look at something." Interrupting himself, he paused to shake his head and, looking annoyed, shifted his attention back to Michael. "Your Honor, I thought we'd decided to keep the lid on this little problem of yours for the good of all concerned. I have to tell you, I was surprised when that story hit the wire services."

"So was I," Michael rejoined quietly. He didn't look at Brady.

Sanchez did, and sighed. "Horner's a pain in the butt sometimes, but he's got good sources. I should have such good sources." He leveled a shrewd black stare at Brady. "You the eyewitness?"

Brady cleared her throat and glanced at Michael. He met her eyes and gave her the slightest of nods. She cleared her throat again and murmured, "Yes."

"You drew that picture?"

Again she nodded. "Yes."

Sanchez shifted back to Michael and said with deceptive mildness, "I wish you'd checked it with me first."

Michael held up his hands as if to say, "Don't look at me; I didn't do it."

"We've had some calls," Sanchez said in a dry tone that was clearly an understatement of heroic proportions. "That's a pretty generic face, apparently. We're checking them all out, just in case. But there's one that's kind of interesting." He reached behind him and produced a large blowup of Brady's sketch of the hit-and-run driver. Holding it up so that both she and Michael could see it, he waited for several pregnant moments and then said, "Tell me what you see."

Michael shrugged. "A face. Just a face."

Brady said more slowly, "A face in a windshield."

Sanchez was nodding. "Right. You see the face, just like everybody else does. Except for this one lady. She's a manicurist, see. Works on people's hands for a living. So that's what she notices. She calls up and says, 'What are you talking about "him" for? That ain't no "him"—that's a "her." ' " Now I want you to look at the hands on that steering wheel and tell me what you see."

Michael whispered, "My God."

Brady felt the room grow colder. Sanchez nodded to her and said to Michael, "Assuming she's got the picture right, our hit man is a woman."

A female officer stuck her head in the door and said, "We're ready for you, Lieutenant."

Sanchez nodded. "Miss Brady—uh, Flynn—if you'll go with the officer here, we'd like to have you look at some pictures and see if you can find the guy who assaulted you. Can you do that?"

Brady blinked at him like someone waking from a trance. "The guy who assaulted me? But I never saw him. I didn't have a chance; he just shoved me into the fountain, and I guess he grabbed my purse as I was falling. I'm sorry." She sounded vague, distracted. Her gaze kept wandering back to the sketch on Sanchez's desk.

"I saw him," Michael said. "I'll have a look at those books if you like." To Brady he said softly, "Still feel like you recognize her?"

She shook herself, as if she felt a sudden chill. "It's so weird. When I thought about 'him' as a woman—it's like when a light bulb burns out, you know? There's this flash, and then nothing. For just an instant I thought... But now it's gone again."

Her eyes were troubled, and her mouth looked fragile. It occurred to Michael that she should have been a comical sight, sitting there in his trench coat with her hair caught up in a red necktie, but for some reason looking at her made his chest ache.

"Look," he said quietly to Sanchez, "since I'm going to be tied up here a while, is there someone who can take her home?"

Brady made a gesture of protest with her hand. "Oh, that's all right; it's only a few blocks to my car—*oh*." She put her fingertips to her lips. "I forgot. My car keys were in my purse. I have spares, but they're at the house."

Michael nodded. "That's all right. We'll get you home." He raised his eyebrows at Sanchez.

The lieutenant gave a put-upon sigh. "Okay, Miss Flynn. Go with the officer. Parkhill, take care of it, will you?"

Brady threw Michael a look, an intense blue look as devastating as a blast from a laser, and without a word got up to follow the policewoman. As he watched her go, Michael noted the chaos inside himself with astonishment. Sanchez's voice came through the tumult like a call from a great distance, and he answered with a distracted, "Hmm?"

"I said, how good is she? How accurate is that picture?"

"As good as a camera," Michael said. "Maybe better."

Sanchez nodded. He sat for a moment, tapping his fingers on the sketch, then got up and went to call through his office door. "Grimball! Morales! Get over to that TV station—KXLA. Pick up Kyle Horner and haul his butt—" He glanced over his shoulder at Michael and amended that. "Be so kind as to *request* that Mr. Horner come and answer a few questions for us, will you, please?" As he came back to his desk he was looking even flintier than usual. "About time we find out what that guy knows that we don't." He looked at his watch. "In the meantime, Your Honor, what do you say we look at some pictures?"

"Hi, are you looking for Brady?"

The visitor started and turned to assess the two people approaching from around the corner. It was hard to tell which one had spoken, but it was the taller, bearded one who held out his hand and added, "We're Brady's neighbors. She's not here right now."

The visitor smiled and firmly shook the offered hand while murmuring regrets.

"I don't know where she is," the bearded one said. The other one frowned and murmured, "She didn't come home last night." The two looked at each other, then back at the visitor, smiling hopefully. "Are you a friend of Brady's?"

The visitor shook her head. "No. Actually, I was interested in some of her drawings."

"Oh, yeah, Brady's so great, isn't she?" The smaller one beamed at the bearded one, who murmured, "Hey, listen, would you like to come up to our place and wait? We could make you some tea, and we just made some persimmon bread."

The visitor politely declined.

Both the small woman and the bearded man looked disappointed. "Well, maybe you can come back?" said one. The other murmured, "Brady'll be really sorry she missed you."

"Oh, I'll be back," the visitor assured them.

They both beamed, first at her and then at each other.

"We'll tell her you were here," said one. The other nodded happily. "We'll be working in our garden. We have to get the manure on before the next rain, so we'll see her when she comes home. We'll be sure and tell her."

"She'll be really glad to show you her pictures. She's so great."

"It's been really nice meeting you. I hope we'll see you again. Take care now."

The bearded one held out a hand with two fingers extended in the shape of a V and rumbled, "Peace."

Back down the hill, just around a bend in the road, the visitor tossed her sunglasses and scarf onto the front seat of her rented car and leaned against it, seething.

So near and yet so far.

As long as those two watchdogs were around, there was no way of getting into the house without being seen. She would just have to find another way. . . .

* * *

"Hi, Brady," the Sunshines chorused, stopping to call through the open window as they crossed the front porch. "We saw you come in."

"We brought your milk," Shyla said.

"And some persimmon bread," Sky put in. "Shyla made it. It's really good."

"Guess what." They looked at each other, obviously bursting with good news. "You had a visitor," Shyla said breathlessly.

"Oh? Who was it?" Brady asked without much interest. There was only one visitor she cared about, and he was no doubt still looking at mug shots at the police station.

"Some woman," Sky said. "She wants to talk to you about your pictures." He was gazing with interest at the red necktie in Brady's hair.

"I really like your tie," Shyla said softly.

"So who was she, do you know? Did she say she liked my work?" But she knew there was no point in trying to rush the Sunshines. They got around to things in their own good time.

"I don't know," Sky said, looking perplexed. "But she said she'd be back," Shyla added, looking radiant.

"Thanks," Brady said with a sigh, taking the milk bottle and the foil-wrapped package from Sky.

"Do you need some more eggs?" Shyla asked. "We thought maybe if Michael was going to be here..."

"No," Brady said, turning away. "Thanks anyway. I don't think Michael will be here again."

"Oh." The Sunshines looked at each other. Shyla hugged Brady and whispered, "I know it's hard. Cancerians need so much patience. But don't give up on him, Brady. I felt such beautiful harmony between you."

Brady didn't even try to answer. Nor did she ask how Shyla knew Michael's sign. She didn't doubt it for one minute, though; Brady didn't pretend to understand all that stuff, but sometimes Shyla could be downright eerie.

Sky gave her a hug, and the Sunshines went back up the hill to their garden. Brady put the milk and the persimmon bread into the refrigerator and went on to her bedroom. She took off the trench coat and started to let it drop to the floor. Then she remembered that it was Michael's and hung it on a hanger in the closet instead. She went into the bathroom and brushed her teeth, then turned on the shower. While the water was heating, she examined her face minutely in the mirror. Her movements were all careful and controlled and had a mechanical sort of stiffness to them, as if she were having to concentrate very hard on what she was doing.

And she was. She remembered feeling like this immediately after her father had died; it had taken all her physical and mental energy just to get through the most elemental tasks. She supposed she must be suffering a similar trauma right now. This was a different sort of loss, but the symptoms were remarkably alike. Back then it had helped to treat herself very gently, as if she were convalescing from a serious illness or injury. Perhaps that was what she needed to do now.

She showered quickly, then dressed in jeans, a bright yellow sweater and an old pair of tennis shoes. Instead of going to the station, she decided to take the day off. It was a beautiful day, and she hadn't been hiking since before the rain; she'd go find her favorite view of the ocean and sit under the cloudless sky and let the wind blow her troubles away.

But though the exercise helped ease the aches in her body, the wind only seemed to bring with it whispers to trouble her mind all the more.

We have nothing in common....

I felt harmony between you....

Which was it? Harmony, or nothing in common? Brady had felt the harmony, but harmony took two, and if Michael hadn't felt it, there wasn't a thing in the world she could do about it.

How depressing, she thought dismally, watching a hawk drift lazily through the sky. To find the person you *know* is the right one for you, and he doesn't feel the same way about you.

For the first time in months she felt anger toward her father for deserting her so unexpectedly. Daddy, where are you when I need you? Damn you, if you hadn't been such a hard-drinkin', hard-livin' Irishman, you'd still be around. You told me I'd know when I found the right one, and you were right. But you forgot to tell me what happens if he doesn't know. So tell me, Daddy—what do I do now?

"Hi, Brady's not here."

Michael turned to watch the Sunshines come down the slope toward him, smiling. Sky had a shovel across his shoulders, and Shyla was holding a rake. A breeze lifted lank strands of flax-colored hair away from their sunburned faces.

So that's what they look like, he thought without surprise. "Not here?" he said, frowning. "That's funny."

"She just went for a walk," Shyla explained.

"She'll probably be back soon," Sky added reassuringly.

"Oh." Since they were both still looking at him in a curiously expectant way, he cleared his throat and said, "I thought I'd see if she wanted a lift to her car. She, uh, had a little bit of a mishap last night. I guess you probably noticed she arrived courtesy of the LAPD."

Sky muttered something noncommittal. Shyla murmured, "We wondered about that." Both of them looked up at the hill, then down at their feet, and then began an intent examination of their respective gardening tools. It occurred to Michael to wonder what, besides vegetables, the Sunshine's might be growing in that garden of theirs.

"Well," he said, "maybe I'll wait around a little while."

"You could wait inside," Sky suggested. Shyla confirmed that with a nod. "Brady wouldn't mind."

"Still not locking her door, is she?" Michael muttered, and asked suddenly, "Where did she go? Do you know?"

The Sunshines looked at each other, smiled and pointed simultaneously. "Up there—toward the ocean."

"Is there a trail?"

The Sunshines nodded.

"Maybe I'll just see if I can find her."

The Sunshines nodded again and smiled. Michael waved to them and went off in the direction they'd indicated. When he turned around to look back at them, they were still standing where he'd left them. They had their arms around each other.

The assassin had left the trail at a spot where an outcropping of boulders and a large live oak formed a natural den. From the top of the lichen-covered rocks she had a clear view of the houses and yards below. She saw the woman striding along the trail, head down, hands tucked in the back pockets of her jeans. In fact, she had the cross hairs of the telescopic sight of her rifle fixed on the flash of red in the woman's straw-colored hair.

It would be so easy.

But it wasn't the right time. There was still that picture. She had to have the picture first.

A sound reached the assassin, carried on the wind—the high, thin cry of a hawk. Slowly lowering the rifle, she lifted her gaze, shading her eyes against the glare of the cloudless sky. There it was, slowly circling. As she watched, it suddenly plummeted from the sky in a hunting dive, disappearing into the scrub. It gave her a primitive thrill to think of those outstretched talons, the small, helpless victim mesmerized by terror, the strike, a squeal of pain quickly extinguished. She knew a kind of ecstasy that was cleaner, purer than sex, almost a spiritual high.

It seemed like an omen. The assassin felt a true affinity for the hawk, and the hawk was telling her that the time to strike was *now*. Such signs could not be ignored. Exhilaration sang in her blood as she lifted the rifle and focused the sight once more on that scrap of blood red. Slowly her finger tightened on the trigger.

A split second later the rifle was back in her lap, and she was left shaking and clammy with unexpended adrenaline. A new figure had moved into her line of fire, and her orders regarding him were very specific.

Once again, it seemed, she would have to wait for another time, another place.

"Hi," Brady said. She stopped in the middle of the path and waited for Michael to reach her. She was out of breath, and her heart was beating so hard it hurt, but it wasn't from physical exertion. "What are you doing here?"

Michael didn't answer until he was directly in front of her, close enough to touch. Then he said softly, "Looking for you."

"Oh," Brady said. "How come?" There was something different about him, she thought. A strange undercurrent of excitement.

"I thought maybe you needed a ride to your car."

She shrugged and looked down at her hands. She'd gathered some dried grasses and flowers and things; now she was systematically tearing them to shreds. "That's okay. I was going to call Kyle."

Michael snorted and smiled grimly. "He might not be free for a while."

"Oh? How come?"

"He's going to be busy telling Lieutenant Sanchez everything he knows about organized crime in this town. Or he

won't tell him—in which case it will all take a lot longer."
There was an odd gleam in his eyes.

Brady lifted what remained of her grasses and let the wind
claim them. "Kyle will never reveal his sources," she said,
watching the chaff drift away. "He'll go to jail first."

"I considered that," Michael said mildly, "and decided
against it." It was a gentle reminder of who and what he
was.

Brady glanced at him, drew an unsteady breath and began to walk slowly down the trail. Michael fell into step beside her. Again she felt that strange energy in him—a kind
of harnessed exuberance.

After a moment he said in a conversational tone, "He had
some interesting things to say about the attempts on my
life."

Brady stopped abruptly and put a hand over her mouth.
Michael gave her a narrow-eyed glance, but continued in
that same deceptively casual manner, "The word, according to Kyle's sources, is that it *was* a mob contract—of a
sort."

Oh, God, how could I have forgotten to tell him? I really
must have been drunk! she thought in horror. "Not to kill
you," she whispered. "Just to..." She let her voice fade into
nothing. Michael wasn't looking at her but into the distance, and never had his jaw looked so hard and uncom-
promising.

"You knew about that?" His voice was very quiet.

Brady swallowed. "Kyle told me. Yesterday."

"Why didn't you tell me?"

"I forgot." She hunched her shoulders, drawing on her
defenses. "So much happened. And I was..."

"Drunk. I know." Michael let his breath out in a long,
slow sigh. "You do know what this means, Brady? If Horner's sources are right, that 'contract' has been fulfilled.
There is no longer any danger to me." She felt him turn his
head to look at her. "It would have been nice to know that

last night.'' His voice developed a ragged edge. "And this morning."

Now she slowly lifted her head to meet his eyes. It was a hard thing to do; she wouldn't have been surprised to hear her neck muscles creak. Even her lips felt stiff. "Are you telling me it would have made a difference?''

Michael's eyes narrowed slightly, but his gaze held hers steadily. The silence became the kind that grates on the eardrums. At last he said very softly, "Yes, I think maybe it would have."

His words broke only the silence; the tension went on stretching, to the breaking point and beyond. Brady swallowed, an exercise so unexpectedly painful that her hand moved involuntarily to her throat. *"Great,"* she whispered, and began to walk away from him down the trail. "That's just great."

She heard him follow her. When she felt his hand close on her arm, she jerked it away and turned furiously on him. *"Why?* What difference does it really make—between us, I mean—with all your other hang-ups?'' She began to tick them off on her fingers. "I was still drunk, according to you. I was—am—still eons younger than you are. We still have nothing whatsoever in common, and there's still this business about commitment. Look, I don't know what you want from me, Michael. I don't think *you* know what you want. In fact, I don't know what the hell you're doing here. You made yourself perfectly clear this morning. It's been a real interesting experience, Judge Snow; now I just wish you'd go away and let me get on with my life!''

She whirled away from him and, after the first few steps, began to run. She was furious with herself, with her tears, her temper, all of which only seemed to prove him right. She *was* too young, too emotional, too impulsive—too different. Damn him for always being so rational, so responsible, so in control.

He caught up with her near a secluded alcove formed by a pile of rocks and a huge oak tree. Catching her by the wrist, he spun her around and pinned her, with a hand on each shoulder, hard against the rough granite. Brady's breath burst from her in a gasp; she stared at Michael with a mixture of fear and amazement.

Because he wasn't in control now. His eyes were the steely gray of storm clouds, his teeth were tightly clenched, his lips a hard, grim line. She could feel the strength and power in him and the violence of his emotions. It was like standing next to an erupting volcano.

"Damn it, Brady." His voice was raw and guttural. "Don't you think I'd like to get on with my life, too? But I can't. I *can't*. This just isn't finished between us. I don't know why that is. Everything you said just now, everything I've said, is true. What I'm doing now doesn't make any sense to me. It's as if I'm operating on two different levels. With every bit of intelligence and common sense I have, I know this is wrong. But somehow, whenever I get near you, I—"

He released her arms and abruptly turned his back to her. She saw him lift a hand to the back of his neck in a gesture that was becoming familiar to her. It was a gesture that betrayed his vulnerability and took away her fear. Aching for him, she said in a small, torn voice, "Why do you have to make it so complicated?"

She saw his shoulders shake with silent, pain-filled laughter. "Brady, I just can't seem to explain myself to you. It's complicated, and it isn't. I don't think I have 'hang-ups,' as you call it, but I guess I just don't have it in me to treat sex casually, either."

Brady took several deep breaths, trying to control the pain inside her, but it was no use. The words came out on the crest of a sob. "What in the world gave you the idea that I *do*?"

Chapter 11

Michael turned slowly to look at her and felt a wave of something that was almost vertigo. Encountering her gaze was like looking into the sea from a great height; if he wasn't careful, he could fall in and drown. And, strangely enough, he was beginning to think that was just what he wanted to do. Then maybe he wouldn't have to think....

He moved closer to her and put his hands on her shoulders, gently kneading. She shrank back against the rock and turned her face away from his scrutiny, but he captured her jaw in his hand and relentlessly pulled her gaze back to meet his.

"Brady? What is that supposed to mean?"

She made a high sound that was half laugh, half whimper. Her eyelids dropped, displacing tears.

"Brady?"

She sniffed and muttered, "Nothing, damn it."

"Look, you're not going to do this to me again. You fight dirty, Miss Flynn—conversational guerrilla warfare. You lob these little bombs at me, then run away and hide. Only this time you aren't going to get away with it!''

Her eyes were open now, mirroring his own confusion. "I don't know what you're talking about."

"Yeah? How about George Washington and Mount Rushmore? How about 'practically a virgin'? Huh? What about that one?''

A laugh burst from her, mixed with tears. "I was *drunk*!"

"Not *that* drunk. How the hell do you get to be practically a virgin? I want to know."

"None of your business." She sniffed again and tried to lift a hand to wipe the moisture from her face.

He restrained her. Cold fury enveloped him; he stared down at the face framed by his hand and grated, "None of my business? After what you put me through? No, Brady, I think—"

But his ruthlessness had aroused her anger. Her eyes opened, and touched him like tongues of blue flame. "You *think*? That's your trouble, Michael, you know? You think too damn much! This isn't a courtroom, and I'm not on trial. Damn you, why don't you for once in your life just *feel*!''

Just feel. But that was the trouble—all he did when he was with her was *feel*. He felt her tears touching his fingers like tiny wet kisses, felt the frantic cadence of her pulse against his palm, felt her chest expand, pushing her breasts against him. And even more than that, he felt his own body heating, swelling, racked by waves of deep tremors. Like a volcano, he thought. And that thought scared him. No one could control a volcano. He was going to explode, and he was afraid of what would happen when he did.

"That's what upsets you about me, isn't it?" Brady whispered, licking her lips. "I make you feel."

He stared down at her through a fog. *Feeling*. Oh, yes, feeling like a balloon about to burst, like a rubber band stretched to the breaking point. Tension screamed through every muscle and nerve in his body. How long could he stand this? He didn't know, but neither did he seem to know how to let go.

"Michael." His name was a broken sigh as her eyelashes drifted down. "It really is okay to feel. It won't kill you."

He heard himself reply with a sound he'd never made before, a low animal growl of need. He felt her lips under his, moved his open mouth slowly back and forth over hers, tasting the salty moisture there and all the while vibrating, shaking, with that awful tension.

"Yes...." Her warm breath sighed into his mouth, mingling with his. "Let go."

With a groan he drove his tongue into her mouth, deeper, deeper, still trembling in all his muscles, still holding himself under tenuous restraint. How far could this go? If he let go now, he was afraid he'd hurt her.

And then she made a sound deep in her throat. Michael tore his mouth from hers. She made another sound, a little cry of deprivation, and tilted her head, reaching blindly for him. It was finally all he could take.

Catching a handful of her hair, he braced her against the assault of his mouth, taking hers with a violence that should have appalled him. He ravaged her with his tongue until her breath became wild, desperate sobs.

When he released her mouth she gave a gasping cry and tried to bury her face in the hollow of his neck, but his hand in her hair denied her. Instead he pulled her head back, baring her throat. He treated that vulnerable arch no more gently than he had her mouth, leaving his mark on the flawless skin. Without raising his head, he slid his arms low around her body and lifted her, bringing her up hard and tight against him.

His body was hot and aching. Her clothing frustrated him; more than that, it enraged him. It was in his way, but he didn't want to let go of her long enough to get rid of it.

Moving his mouth down her neck, he caught the edge of her sweater in his teeth and growled, "Take it off."

Unhesitatingly obedient, she reached down to grasp the bottom of the sweater and pull it over her head. She wasn't wearing a bra. With her arms stretched high and the sweater covering her face, Michael lifted her and covered one erect nipple with his mouth. At the first brush of his tongue, he felt her body quake with great racking shudders. He heard her whimpers of frustration as she struggled to free herself from the confines of the sweater. With a surge of primitive masculine exultation, he pulled the tenderest part of her breast deep into the furnace of his mouth, then left it aching while he caught the other between his lips and tormented it ruthlessly with his teeth and tongue.

Free at last of the sweater, Brady clutched at his shoulders and gasped his name. His reply was inarticulate; he was beyond words. He felt her hands on his head, burrowing through his hair; her head was thrown back, and her breath tore through her in tight, quick gasps. When he altered his grip on her, catching the backs of her thighs in his hands, she lifted her legs willingly and brought them around his hips.

And now he found a new frustration. He could hold her tightly to his body, press himself hard against her, make her writhe against the pressure of his masculinity, make her feel his heat and hunger—but it wasn't what he wanted. He resented the barriers that protected her from him. He wanted her open to him. He wanted to be inside her.

Lowering her feet to the ground, he pressed her back against the rock and pinned her there, using only the pressure of his mouth on her throat. Barely aware that she was helping him, he tore open her jeans and yanked them roughly over her hips, then caught impatiently at the thin barrier of her panties. He didn't bother to finish the job then, but instead sought her feminine softness with his fingers.

He lifted his head and looked around, becoming fully aware of his surroundings for the first time. A secluded den, walled and canopied by rocks, trees and brush—private enough. A bed of moist earth and new grass. Not the most comfortable of accommodations, but with the part of his mind that was still capable of rational thought, he knew that if he took the time to find real walls and a real bed, reason would reclaim him. What he was doing was so savage, so primitive, that it had to happen like this—or not at all.

Her sweater was lying on the ground where she had dropped it. Without hesitation he jerked his own sweater over his head and let it fall; a moment later his shirt joined the pile. He said her name. "Brady."

"Yes," she said, and put her hands on his belt buckle. "Please."

He made a bed of their discarded clothing and eased her gently down. She lay looking up at him, eyes glazed, lips moist and bruised, one hand half covering a breast still wet from his mouth. When she saw his nakedness her breath caught and her eyes darkened, but though he recognized the look of feminine apprehension, he knew that it would make no difference—to either of them.

Her eyes clung to him, half hungry, half fearful, as he took her hand and moved it out of his way. His own hand took its place, lingered at her breast for a moment, then swept slowly down over her belly and slipped between her thighs. They tightened reflexively, then responded to the pressure of his hand and parted. He stroked the insides of her thighs, first one, then the other, opening her fully to his touch.

She gasped when she felt the intrusion of his fingers, and he leaned forward and stifled the gasp with his mouth, then slid his fingers deeply inside her, searching for her body's secret pools of liquid heat. Quickly then, he brought her to melting readiness. Her body arched and writhed against his hand; her breath tore through her chest in frantic little sobs.

He held her open with his fingers and fitted himself to her, then raised his head and looked down at her.

Her eyes were closed, the lids misted with a sheen of perspiration. Without opening them, she whispered, "Michael." He felt her hands on his back as they swept down to rest above the base of his spine. "It's all right."

And so he pressed into her, releasing a long, ragged breath as he felt her tender body break and give way to his. He knew a moment of pure anguish, and might have withdrawn then if she hadn't said something that irrevocably shattered his control.

With her chest heaving beneath him, her body pinioned by his and her breath coming in sobs, she still managed to gasp, "Michael, it's all right, it's all right. I love you."

With a deep-throated cry of bitter regret, he drove deep, all the way to the core of her body. He didn't lose control—he gave it up, surrendered it. Unconditionally. The resulting explosion was agonizing, wrenching, and its aftermath was sublime peace.

In that aftermath, as he lay spent and heavy with his face in the warm hollow of her neck, he felt her hands touch his back like tender blessings and heard her whisper, "Yes."

Brady held him and stroked his back, breathing in shallow sips of air and trying not to cry. She couldn't allow herself to cry, because she knew Michael wouldn't understand. She felt ravaged and torn, but not in body; the physical discomforts she felt were minute and inconsequential. She ached in the very depths of her being, not for herself but for him. For Michael, for this man she held in her arms. For this man she loved.

She had felt it all—the tension and turmoil, the struggle, the release. There had been an explosion in her, too, of a different sort—an explosion of love, protective and fierce; an explosion of joy so profound it seemed almost a miracle. Now she felt such awe that she trembled with it. Awe that this intensely private and complex man had given himself up to her. And such tenderness—tenderness that swelled inside her until she felt she would burst with it. Such overwhelming emotions demanded the release of tears, but she could not, dared not, allow herself to cry.

Because she knew that what Michael was feeling right now was not joy or anything like it. What Michael was feeling was anguish.

As soon as he could, he lifted his weight off her, raising himself on one elbow to look down at her. The shame he felt must have shown, because Brady caught his face between her hands and said with hoarse urgency, "No, no, don't be sorry. I swear to God if you say, 'I'm sorry,' I'll kill you."

He cleared his throat, but found that he couldn't speak. It was just as well; it made it easier not to think. He closed his eyes and slowly lowered his mouth to brush her lips. Then he pulled back and touched her face lightly, wonderingly, with the backs of his fingers. Her eyes closed, and her mouth formed a slightly blurred smile. Beneath him he felt her body relax. When he suddenly reached up to pull his red necktie from her hair, she caught her lower lip with her teeth.

"I hurt you," he said hoarsely, watching the tie as he trailed it across her breasts and belly, down to the junction of their bodies. "Brady, I—"

She didn't contradict him, but simply laid a finger across his lips, silencing him. He sighed, eased himself away from her body and rolled over. After a moment he sat up and drew his hand across her abdomen, cradling the tender place between her thighs.

"Come on," he said, his throat still feeling like sandpaper. "Let's get dressed. I want to get you into a nice warm tub." He gave her a hand up and helped her dress, marveling at the fact that there was no shyness, no reserve, in her at all.

Funny, no matter how many times he'd made love to Helen, she'd always made him feel as if he'd somehow vio-

lated her. But this woman—the woman he'd practically
raped—made him feel as if he'd given her a rare and wonderful gift.

Brady drifted in a somnolent haze beneath a frothy cloud
of rainbow bubbles, listening to the pounding rush of water from the shower next door. There was, she reflected,
something inherently masculine about showers. Why that
should be she didn't know; she preferred showers herself.
But her bathroom had a shower over a bathtub, while the
other bathroom had a stall shower. A big stall shower—big
enough for two.

What would happen, she wondered, if she were to go into
the other bathroom, slip into the shower, put her arms
around Michael's body from behind and fit herself to his
curves and hollows? She wanted to smooth her hands over
the planes of his belly, make lathery swirls in his body hair.
She wanted to hold him, touch him, look at him.

She'd had such brief glimpses of his body—that day he'd
come out of Sean's bedroom wearing a towel, and then a
little while ago. She'd thought he was beautiful, but he
frightened her a little, too, mostly because of the way looking at him made her feel inside. Now, though, she wanted
to look at him without shyness; she wanted to know his
body, every inch of it, as well as she knew her own. She
wanted to know what his skin tasted like, and how he liked
to be touched.

She stirred in the caressing water and gave her head an
impatient shake. The tender place between her thighs had
begun to throb, and in spite of the soothing warmth that
surrounded them, her breasts had grown tight and achy.

It was hard to think of Michael right now. Thinking about
him hurt her in so many ways, but most of all she hurt *for*
him. He was a controlled man who'd lost control; a highly
principled man who'd violated his principles; a rational man
who'd acted irrationally; an honorable man who'd be-

haved, at least in his own assessment, with dishonor. Would he ever be able to forgive himself? Would he ever forgive her?

In some ways she knew him very well, and in some ways she didn't know him at all. There was so much she wanted to learn about him. Please God, she prayed, let him give me the chance.

The shower next door drummed against the wall like the sound of distant surf. Brady closed her eyes and thought of Michael's big square hands making soapy swirls on his dusky skin, but though she yearned to do so, she didn't join him. After all, Michael was a very private man; he'd undoubtedly rather be alone.

The shower curtain slid back on its rod, startling her out of a semidoze. She opened her eyes to find Michael leaning against the wall, watching her. The expression on his face was his judge's look—the one of sleepy, heavy-lidded assessment she had grown so familiar with—but all resemblance to the aloof figure in judicial robes ended there. He'd come straight from his shower, bringing with him a steamy aura of masculinity; his skin was heat-flushed, his hair spiky and wet, and drops of water shimmered on his chest and shoulders. He had a towel tucked negligently around his hips, and he stood with his arms crossed, hands tucked into his armpits. He looked lean and lazy, but in his eyes there was something dark and shadowed, something Brady, with her new awareness of him, had no trouble recognizing as pain.

She'd made a reflexive movement when he'd pulled the curtain back; now she relaxed and let her head fall back against the tub.

"Are you all right?" His voice was quiet but gravelly.

Brady nodded and murmured, "Yes. I'm fine."

"You're not sore?"

She shook her head. "No."

"You're lying." His mouth was a bitter line. "I know I hurt you."

It became too hard to hold that smoky gaze, so she looked down at her chest and blew softly, stirring a little eddy in the bubbles that covered her breasts. "Hurt is a subjective thing," she said finally. "There really are some kinds that aren't important."

He made a sound, and when she looked at him she saw that he'd covered the lower part of his face with his hand. He drew air deep into his lungs, then gave his head a little shake and said, "You are an amazing woman. I don't think I understand you very well. I think I may have—" his mouth curved in a smile of irony "—misjudged you. You see, you seem so uncomplicated, so casual about things—like relationships. Like sex. And yet I know now that it's been a very long time since you've been with a man. I'd have said never, except for what you said about being—"

"Practically a virgin?" Brady murmured, smiling down into the bubbles.

"Yes," he said, not smiling at all. "I need to know about that. I need to know about a lot of things. You have a way, you know, of dropping these remarks and then leaving them unexplained."

"I don't mean to," she said, watching her hand play hide-and-seek. "It's just that some things, personal philosophies, sexual track records, aren't very easy to talk about. They don't come up all that often in conversation, you know."

"I know." His mouth flirted with a smile. "Unless..."

"You're drunk," Brady finished with a breathy spurt of laughter.

"Yes," he said, serious again. "But you're not drunk now, and I really need to know some things about you, Brady."

"Ask me," she said softly. "Anything."

"Are you sure?"

"Yes."

He took a deep breath. Without his appearing to move a muscle, his posture altered subtly, becoming a defensive stance; his face—his jaw, his mouth, his eyes—hardened imperceptibly.

Brady thought, He's put his armor on. I wonder why.

"A little while ago, up there, you said something. I want to know why. You said—" He filled his chest, then punched the words bluntly into the steamy air. "You said you loved me. Why?"

"Because," Brady said with quiet simplicity, "I do."

After a while he made a sound, perplexed and exasperated, and sat down on the edge of the tub near her feet. "Brady," he said as he rubbed a hand across his face, "that's impossible. You don't even know me. You've know me, what? Four, five days now?"

Brady smiled. "Well, actually I've been watching you a lot longer than that, but it doesn't matter. Five days is enough. Five minutes is enough."

"That's crazy."

"For some people, maybe. Not for me. Dad said I'd know when it happened, and he was right." She moved in the water, laying her head back and drawing one knee up.

Michael watched her leg rise from the bubbles in fascinated silence, as if it were some strange, exotic life-form, then cleared his throat and shook himself. "Your dad was right?" he said, frowning. "About what?"

"About love, sex," Brady said lazily. "That sort of thing." The water was beginning to have a strange effect on her. She was feeling both languorous and restless, if that was possible, while her thumping heart sent waves of heat into her cheeks and pulse-echoes resounded through the most sensitive parts of her body.

Plus her hands were beginning to prune. So she lifted them out of the water and, while she was at it, raised her arms over her head in a languid stretch.

Michael's eyes followed the movement of her arms, touched her hot cheeks and rested briefly on the place where the water lapped at the tops of her breasts. His hand stirred idly through the water, caught a puff of soap bubbles and carried it to the top of her knee. He balanced it there, then watched it slide slowly down her thigh. "Tell me," he said huskily, "about your dad."

Brady began to play with the soap trail on her thigh, concentrating on that while she talked so she wouldn't have to look at Michael. "He raised me, you know. I never knew my mother; she died when I was just a baby. But it wasn't really as if I grew up without a mother, because my dad was both. He even made clothes for me, can you believe that?"

She glanced up at him then and saw that there were smile creases at the corners of his eyes. She felt a wave of something that stung the backs of her lids, but swallowed it, waited a moment, then went on.

"Of course, there were some things he just couldn't do for me—like teach me how to be a girl. So most of the way through school I was pretty backward socially. I couldn't even date until I was seventeen, and in this town that means you might as well be dead. By the time I was a senior in high school, I was feeling pretty rebellious. It wasn't that I hadn't dated, but, well, it just seemed like I was probably the only one in school who hadn't . . ." She dropped a hand over her eyes and laughed. "Isn't it funny? Talking about it makes me feel just like I did then—embarrassed, sort of. Well, anyway, by the time my senior prom rolled around, I'd about had it with being the last virgin in the class. So I made up my mind to do something about it."

Michael made a noise. She glanced at him, but he shook his head and murmured gravely, "Go on."

She cleared her throat. "Well, it was your basic big evening—we had a limo, I had a new dress, put my hair up."

"The portrait," Michael muttered. "The one your dad—"

"Yes," Brady said. "I was mad about that, too. But anyway, the evening went pretty much as you'd expect. I didn't even like the guy that much—he was just somebody who asked me to the prom—but I didn't really care. I just wanted to prove something. I don't know." She had to stop finally. It wasn't something she'd ever told anyone before, so she hadn't known it was going to be so painful. After a while she took a deep breath and went on, but without looking at Michael. His eyes were just too intense.

"What I didn't count on was that my dad would be waiting up for me. He took one look at me and knew what I'd done. I took one look at him and started to cry. I was hurting, and I expected to die. I was sure he'd kill me. But he just put his arms around me and held me and let me cry, and then he got me a washcloth for my face and a Kleenex for my nose and told me to blow. Then he said, in his blunt, matter-of-fact way, 'Brady-girl, what you've already given away is gone for good—there's no sense cryin' over it. It's what you've still got to give that's important. And there's only one good reason in the world to give it, and that's when your heart tells you it's right. And don't be in a hurry, because it'll come when it comes.'" Brady sniffed and put a hand across her eyes. "So of course I said, 'But, Daddy, how will I know?' and he just said, 'You'll know.'" She shrugged and finished simply, "So I waited. And he was right. When it came, I knew."

There was a long silence. Eventually Michael drew a breath and said, "I think I'd like to have known your father."

"Yes," Brady said. "You'd have liked each other."

Michael stood abruptly. Brady looked up at him, alarmed by the fierce, dark look on his face. "Where are you going?"

"Out." With his hand on the door, he paused to look down at her. His face showed deep lines of strain, but his eyes held an elusive twinkle of mischief. "Your bubbles are all gone," he said quietly, and went out.

He knew what he should do. He knew what he *had* to do. What he'd already done was indefensible; to do any more would be unforgivable. She loved him. Of all the reasons he had for resisting her, that was the ultimate one.

Before she'd said those words, he'd thought it might be possible. He'd come out of that police station feeling about a million pounds lighter, knowing he was free of the terrible burden of those death threats. For the first time in weeks he didn't have to worry that every breath he took might be his last. He didn't have to worry that some innocent bystander might be caught in the cross fire. He'd come looking for Brady because he'd felt free to explore the possibilities of what might happen between them. That was all. But he hadn't realized how close he was to the breaking point. He hadn't been prepared for the explosion, and he was going to have a hard time living with that.

But dear God, she loved him. And he knew she was talking about the real thing—the all-out, unconditional, forever kind of love. Commitment with a capital *C*. And he just couldn't give her that—didn't even want to think about it. Which was ironic, when you stopped to think about it. He'd spoken of commitment; she hadn't. But he'd already made that mistake, and he didn't want a repeat performance.

He'd thought about remarrying, and he'd thought about what it would take to make a success of a relationship. He knew that at the bottom of it, first and foremost, there had to be a good solid foundation of *friendship*, the kind that would get them through the rough times, the times when the pressures of his job got in the way. He'd never had that with Helen. And he couldn't see how he could ever have that with Brady; they just didn't have anything to build a friendship on. They didn't have the same tastes; they didn't think alike;

they had different backgrounds; they came from different eras. They had nothing in common.

Then why, a quiet inner voice inquired, do you like her so much?

Because he did like her. He liked being with her. He liked hearing her talk. God help him, he even liked her hair. Was it just the chemistry between them that made him look forward so much to seeing her? Or could it possibly be something more?

Well, the quiet voice suggested, don't you think you should give yourself a chance to find out?

He was standing there in the middle of the bedroom, wearing his slacks and holding his shirt in his hands, contemplating the grass stains, when Brady came and stood in the doorway. She was wearing a towel. Her feet made wet tracks on the wood floor.

Michael just stood and looked at her. She looked back at him and said, "Where are you going?"

He lifted the shirt, opened his mouth, closed it again and tossed the shirt on the bed.

She tried a new question. "Why did you run out like that?"

He frowned at her. "Run out of where?"

"The bathroom. You acted like you couldn't stand to look at me."

Her eyes were bright, her hair so vibrant that it seemed to have a life of its own. She held the towel clutched casually to her breasts; it was draped low in back, baring the gentle curve of her spine.

Michael cleared his throat and said harshly, "Don't be ridiculous."

Her voice was very soft. "Am I being ridiculous, Michael?"

"Yes." Give it a chance, the voice said. He began to move toward her. "You are being ridiculous."

"Then why," she asked, "are you going?"

"Because..." His own voice had grown husky. "I thought I should."

"What if I don't want you to go?"

Stay, the voice said. Take a chance. Take the risk.

"Then I guess I might reconsider," he finally said aloud.

"Please," she whispered. "Stay."

"If I stay," he said softly, "I won't sleep in the guest room. Or on the couch."

"I should hope not." She took a step toward him.

He suddenly held up a hand, stopping her in her tracks. "Hold it right there." A thought had just come to him, something that filled him with effervescence, something that felt remarkably like youth and moonlight and champagne. She was gazing at him, tilting her head quizzically, so he tried to explain it to her.

"Brady, we came into this thing in the middle. The problem is, I haven't been able to figure out the story. I don't know where we are, or what's happening, or what's going to happen. Hush," he admonished her gently when she opened her mouth to interrupt him. "I think that what I would like to do is take us back to chapter one. Well, maybe a little farther along than that. But I want us to back up a bit." He took a deep breath. "I'm just an old-fashioned guy, Brady. If it's not too late, what I really want to do is court you."

He saw a dawning look of wonder in her face. "Court me? You mean like . . . date?"

He considered that. "I don't know," he said at last. "Dating has more of an experimental flavor to it, you know what I mean? But courting, that suggests *intent*." He began to walk slowly toward her.

She licked her lips and murmured, "Intent?"

He stopped directly in front of her, looked down into her eyes and had to fight another slight wave of dizziness. "I *intend*," he said softly, touching one bare shoulder with the tips of his fingers, "to make love to you again. But slowly this time, and from the very beginning." He drew his fingers lightly along the ridge of her shoulder, barely brushing the translucent down that gave her skin the texture of softest velvet, then followed the vibrant cord of her neck to the underside of her jaw. He felt her swallow.

"Tonight?" she whispered.

He rubbed the soft place under her chin with his thumb. Her lips parted, and he bent to touch them lightly with his. "That depends," he said, "on you."

"On me?"

"Uh-huh. For a couple of reasons. On whether or not you're protected, for one thing. I'd assumed you were, but now I'm fairly certain you're not—are you?"

She shook her head and gave an embarrassed little cough. "Well, no. But then, don't forget, I'm Irish. I was brought up Catholic, so I have a pretty good idea of when it's okay. And . . . it's okay."

He gave her a stern look. "Positive?"

"Yes."

"Okay—for now." Now it was his turn to cough. "The other thing that depends on you is how you feel after this afternoon."

"Oh." her voice was breathy; he felt her lips form a smile. "Well, that depends."

"On what?"

"On how gentle you intend to be."

His smile joined hers. "As gentle as you want me to be." He pulled back but kept his fingers on her face, delicately stroking her lower lip with his thumb. "Now I want you to go and get dressed, okay? And don't come out until I call for you."

She nodded. Her eyes had a slightly glazed look. "What should I wear?"

He took her by the shoulders and turned her firmly toward the door. "Surprise me," he murmured, touching a kiss to the damp nape of her neck.

* * *

Dusk comes early in November, even in Southern California, and with it an autumn chill. The Santa Anas had died a natural death; soon the coastal mountains would wear a shroud of fog.

The assassin watched the curtains fall across the windows and the lights come on in the house below, and knew again the special frustration of the predator who had missed her chance to strike. There was no point in waiting any longer; the girl would not be alone again tonight.

But there was still tomorrow, and in the assassin's mind, the seeds of a plan were already growing.

Chapter 12

Brady was pacing the floor of her bedroom when the knock came. Though she'd been waiting for it, it startled her, causing her already uneven heartbeat to skip. She cleared her throat, wiped damp palms down the front of her thighs and called, "Come in."

She couldn't ever remember being this nervous, even the night of her senior prom.

The door opened, and Michael just stood there looking at her, not saying anything. His collar was open, and his sleeves were rolled to just below the elbows. His hair glinted at the temples with silver lights. His stance was relaxed, graceful, self-assured—and the expression on his face was slightly stunned.

"Well," Brady said breathlessly, "I guess I did, huh?"

Michael gave himself a little shake and said, "Did what?"

"Surprise you."

He laughed softly. "Yes, I guess you did."

She was wearing black, a simple long-sleeved sweater dress that clung to her lithe body like a second skin. It came to just below her knees and had a neckline that was straight across in front but fell in the back almost to the waist, leaving no trace of doubt as to what she could be wearing under it. She'd tucked and twisted her hair into a simple style high on her head, except for a few curls that would not be subdued and brushed her nape and the delicate shells of her ears. Her only adornment, her one concession to the brilliant colors he knew she loved, was a scarf, worn loosely draped around her shoulders, a shimmering swirl of red, turquoise and gold.

Brady's heart slowed to a hard, heavy pace as she watched Michael stroll toward her. His manner was leisurely, unhurried.

"You are a witch," he said, touching her hot cheek with the back of one finger. The look in his eyes was smoky, his voice a low rumble. "The most bewitching of witches."

Yes, a witch, whose eyes were translucent porcelain, almond-shaped, with an exotic tilt. As he tucked her hand in the curve of his elbow, Michael smiled down into those eyes and murmured, "I think I know what's happened to me. I bumped headlong into an Irish witch, and to get even she cast a spell on me."

Brady looked up past the bulk of his shoulder and the strong, square ridge of his jaw, and found the smile lines at the corners of his mouth and eyes. "Me?" she said on a shallow breath. "Get even for what?"

He touched her lip with a gentle finger. "I hurt you," he said. "Remember? And I haven't been the same since."

Brady couldn't think of an answer to that because they had come into the living room, and for a few minutes words simply failed her. She stopped, and her mouth formed a silent, "Oh." At last she looked up at Michael and murmured, "Which one of us is the witch?"

He laughed and squeezed her hand. "Come on. I think our table's ready."

The room was lit by fire and candlelight. The coffee table was covered with a cloth and set with brass candlesticks and Brady's mother's wedding china. At each place was a plate of crisp green salad, and in the center of the table stood a single covered serving dish.

"What—" Brady began, but he gently hushed her.

"All in good time," he murmured as he led her to her place at the table and settled her onto a cushion on the floor. Before sitting down himself, he drew a plastic bucket out from under the table. "Ah," he said with satisfaction. "It's chilling nicely."

"Wine," Brady said faintly. "I'd forgotten I even had that."

"Not a bad wine, actually." Michael squinted critically at the label as he worked with the stopper. It gave with a faint pop. "I couldn't find wineglasses," he went on, picking up a water tumbler and smiling at her across its rim. "These will have to do, unless you know some special incantation?"

Brady just smiled back and shook her head. Clever repartee was beyond her now. She felt as if she was moving in a dream.

Please God, don't let my hands shake, Michael thought as he poured the wine. "To new beginnings," he murmured, lifting his glass. When she had clinked hers against his, he looked into her eyes and added somberly, "and to taking chances." There was a little silence. "You had some nice greens in the refrigerator," he finally observed as he poured dressing liberally over his salad.

"Yes," Brady said. "The Sunshines keep me well supplied."

"Here, this is yours." He nudged a small pitcher closer to her. "I know you don't like Italian dressing."

Brady looked in the pitcher and stared up at Michael in awe. "Ranch," she said feebly. "My favorite. How did you…?'' She shook her head and gazed blindly down at her salad, wondering how she was going to manage a single bite.

Why was he doing this? Everything he did, every word he spoke, only made her love him more. But she couldn't possibly love him more; she was full to bursting with love for him already. If she loved him any more, she'd have to explode.

In an effort to get hold of herself, she asked, ''What's in there?'' She pointed to the covered dish.

With a grand gesture, Michael swept off the lid. Brady burst out laughing.

''Omelets—what else?'' they said together, and laughed some more. To Brady, the laughter felt a little trembly, but good—so good.

''I like you in black,'' Michael said. ''I've never seen you wear it before.''

They had finished eating and were sipping wine, watching the reflections the candles made in each other's eyes. Michael had pointedly refused to add more than a meager dollop to Brady's glass, teasing her about her ''two-beer limit.''

''Thanks,'' Brady said. ''I don't really wear black much. I got this dress to wear dancing. Black is *the* color to wear dancing.'' She smiled, and the light danced in her eyes. ''I really like bright colors.''

''I know,'' Michael said softly. ''I like you in bright colors, too.'' He reached across the table and pulled the scarf slowly away from her shoulders. ''But like this…'' He stopped, because suddenly words seemed inadequate. In stark black, with her hair pulled back away from her Madonna's face, with her long, graceful neck, her enchantress's eyes… ''You really are incredibly beautiful.'' He said it wonderingly, as if it were a revelation to him, and in a way it was. He was suddenly realizing that she was the most beautiful woman he'd ever known, beautiful in a very special way, uniquely her own.

She was gazing at him. "Beautiful?" she whispered. "Me?"

"Hasn't anyone ever told you that before?"

She shook her head. "No, but that's all right. I'm glad you're the first. Because I think you are, too."

"Hey," Michael said laughing. "You're not supposed to say that."

"Why not? It's true. I've always thought that."

"Always?" His eyes twinkled at her. "For almost a week now, you mean?"

"Oh, no, much longer than that. I've been drawing you for months, didn't you know that? I have a whole notebook full of pictures of you—or I had. I've always loved your face. And now, I think you're beautiful."

"Well." Michael coughed. "I guess that's a first."

"You're embarrassed!" Brady gave a breathy little giggle of sheer delight. "Hasn't anyone ever told *you* that before?"

He shook his head, coughed again and got to his feet. "Hey, you know what, I forgot to put on the music."

There was an endearing touch of awkwardness in his movements as he walked to the old record player and turned it on. Brady watched him place the needle carefully in its groove and felt herself fill to overflowing with tenderness.

"Dad's old records," she said as the mellow sound of a saxophone filled the room, and she smiled at him. "That's not exactly what I'd call dancing music."

"No?" He came toward her, holding out his hand. "Have you ever tried dancing to music like this?" When she shook her head, he murmured, "Good, another first," and pulled her to her feet.

They stood facing each other while the music and the candlelight closed in around them, soft and warm.

"You know how it goes," Michael said huskily. "I know you do. You've seen old Doris Day movies."

Her breath caught. "You like Doris Day movies?"

He nodded. "Do you?"

She nodded.

"Will wonders never cease? *Another* first."

Brady gave a soft gurgle of laughter. "Maybe we're on a roll here. How do you feel about baseball?"

He groaned. "Sorry." His eyes crinkled at the corners, then darkened. "Brady," he rasped, "put your arms around me."

She lifted them high, and he felt her touch like a sultry whisper on the back of his neck. He put his hands on her waist, marveling at the slenderness of it. Then he drew her in until, inch by inch, she touched him all along the front of his body.

"Now," he said, feeling as if his chest was full of champagne bubbles, "just move with me."

He began to sway, and she swayed with him. Her thighs slid sinuously over his; her waist moved beneath his hands with supple grace. Her breasts pressed against his chest; he felt the warmth of them through the soft fabric of her dress and the thin fabric of his shirt. With her head tilted back, she watched him as if her life was in his eyes.

"'Mood Indigo'" She crooned the words, not quite singing. "That's what your eyes are. Indigo. They're so dark. I was surprised to find out that they were blue."

"And you have witch's eyes." A chuckle welled up inside him as a song title came into his mind. "You have that old devil moon in your eyes."

Her eyes went wide, then tilted with her smile. "You *know* I'd have to know that song. I think Dad probably sang me to sleep with that one."

"I guess that explains it." *Bewitched . . . devil moon . . .* Something throbbed in the pit of his stomach like primitive drums.

"Brady," he said huskily, "do something for me." Looking down into her eyes, he felt a surge of emotion so powerful that it all but swamped him, and he whispered raggedly, "Take your hair down."

Slowly, in a sensual daze, she began to take the pins from her hair. It seemed an incredibly intimate thing to be doing—more intimate even than undressing before him. She didn't take her eyes from his. She had to arch backward slightly, and to support her he moved one hand higher on her back, while with the other he held her lower body tightly against him. She felt his desire, and the throbbing pressure became part of her.

The last of the pins came free. Her hair tumbled over his hand, sweet-smelling and as fresh as a cascade of apple blossoms. He turned his hand in it, winding his fingers through it, then lifted both hands and, with his fingers, combed it back away from her face.

Her eyes were closed, her lips slightly parted. As he looked down at that lush, sensuous mouth, his hunger twisted audibly in his belly. He had to remind himself, Slowly, go slowly now.

So he just touched her with the tips of his fingers, spanning her face from temples to jaw, brushing her full, quivering lips with his thumb. He drew his fingers slowly downward over the edge of her jaw, following the graceful sweep of her throat to where it met the neckline of her dress. Hooking one finger in the soft, stretchy knit, he pulled it forward and down, just far enough to bare one silken shoulder. When at last he lowered his head to touch her with his lips, he heard the sigh of her breath, then felt the trembling weight of her fingers in his hair.

The music was forgotten; they swayed now to rhythms of their own making.

He opened his mouth and blew softly on her skin, then touched it with his tongue, delicately tasting. Her head tilted like a wilting flower, offering the sensitive cords of her neck.

Her fingers threaded silkily through his hair to rest on the back of his neck, just inside the collar of his shirt.

"Michael." Her voice was a shallow whisper. "Will you do something for me?"

"Mmm?" He raised his head to look at her, but found that her eyes were still closed.

"Please, take off your shirt."

"No." At his murmured denial, her eyes flew open; he touched each eyelid with a kiss, closing them again. Reaching up to capture her hand, he brought it to his mouth, then tucked it between their bodies, in the spot where their heartbeats met in wild, opposing rhythms. "I don't want to let go of you. You take it off for me.

She gave a little laughing groan. "I don't know. My fingers feel funny."

"Funny how?" He brought her other hand to his mouth, but this time he made love to her hand, laving the hollow of her palm with his warm tongue, probing the sensitive valley between each finger, taking the tip of each finger deep into the liquid heat of his mouth. When he had finished, he blew softly across her fingers and whispered, "Better?" She didn't answer, so he held her hand against his chest and murmured, "Brady?"

She swallowed, then mumbled indistinctly, "What?"

"Is your hand all right now?"

"No, but whatever it was, it's spread to my knees."

"Don't worry about your knees. I'll hold you. Just concentrate on the buttons, one at a time."

It was hard. Her fingers shook so badly that she wanted to weep with frustration. Michael didn't help or hurry her. He just held her, one hand a firm pressure on the base of her spine, the other on the nape of her neck, gently stroking. He swayed slightly to the music so that their bodies moved against each other with an exquisite friction that sent heat searing deep inside.

Finally the last button she could reach above the waist-band of his slacks came free in her hands. She looked up into his eyes and slowly pulled the shirttails free. Holding on to his smoky indigo gaze as if to a beacon, she found and dealt with the last buttons. Then, almost reverently, she allowed her eyes to close and, placing her hands flat against his belly, leaned her forehead against his chest. She sighed and whispered, "I've been wanting to do this."

"Feel free," he said raggedly, "to do whatever you'd like."

She made a little chuckling sound of pure pleasure and nuzzled at the indentation in the center of his chest. Then, pulling back a little so she could look at him, she began to push her hands upward, counting his ribs, measuring the resilient muscle, fanning her fingers across the flat planes below his shoulders. She smiled at him, her eyes slumber-ous, and drew her fingernails lightly downward. He sucked in air. She flattened her hands, gently rubbing her palms over his taut masculine nipples. Her eyes widened in surprise.

"Oh," she whispered, entranced. "I didn't know yours did that, too."

His belly tightened, and his chest jerked with tender laughter. "Oh, yes, mine do that, too." He nudged her forehead with his chin. "Are yours doing that right now?"

She nodded. "Uh-huh."

"Show me."

His voice was a gritty whisper, rasping over her skin like sandpaper, sending shivers of electricity racing along every nerve path in her body. Barely able to breathe, she caught her lower lip in her teeth and looked into his eyes. She saw firelight reflected in them, and even hotter flames blazed in their depths. It was those inner flames that touched her cheeks and made them burn.

She lifted her hands to the neckline of her dress and pulled it slowly down.

She heard the long sigh of his released breath and felt his hands on her shoulders. His eyes rested briefly on her mouth, then moved downward, leaving a trail of fire wherever they touched her. He drew his fingers down her arms, then slipped them between her arms and body and just brushed the outer curve of her breasts with his palms. "Yes," he sighed, tracing the silken underside with his thumbs. "I see." And then, drawing his thumbs across the pebble-hard tips, he demanded, "Tell me . . . how it feels."

Her breath was a hot weight in her chest. Her lips felt swollen. She closed her eyes, swayed and mumbled indistinctly, "Hurts, but in a funny way. Sharp, but good. And it makes me hurt inside." She pressed her hand against her abdomen and splayed her fingers wide. "But, different." Her hand moved, unconsciously rubbing. "Good."

Still cradling the tender weight of her breasts in his hands, Michael lowered his head, lightly touched one rosebud tip with his lips, circled it slowly with his tongue and finally drew it deep into his mouth. She made a high, whimpering sound, and when he took his mouth away she moved her hand convulsively to cover what he'd left so exposed and vulnerable. When he had treated the other breast to the same exquisite torture, he held her hands away and said thickly, "Now. Tell me now."

"Cold," she muttered, sounding vexed.

He chuckled, a deep-chested rumble, and, still holding her hands away from her body, drew her to him so slowly that her nipples first brushed soft, crisp hair and then were buried in it, touching his skin like tiny wet kisses. He pulled her still closer and became lost in the wonder of holding her, all of her, naked and trembling in his arms.

"Michael." Her arms came around him, and she clung to him with a kind of desperation, hiding her hot face against his chest. "I can't—"

He chuckled again, a sound of masculine pleasure, and, weaving his fingers through her hair, ruthlessly lifted her face out of its refuge and tilted it, exposing it to the sweet tortures of his mouth. Her eyes were closed, her cheeks flushed with desire. Her lips were parted; they looked moist and ripe, like some exotic fruit. He tasted them with his tongue and found them slightly salty from their recent contact with his own skin.

She moaned softly when he pulled away and turned her head, searching for his mouth, wanting his mouth and the deep, all-consuming penetration of his tongue. But he teased her, laving her lips, outside, inside, sliding his tongue across her teeth, leaving her tingling with cooling moisture and gasping with frustrated yearning. She thought she would burst. She wanted to scream with the agony of it. Her whole body was aching, trembling, throbbing, melting. And when she thought she would surely go mad, he gave a low growl and covered her open mouth, stifled her desperate whimpers and filled the hot, hungry void with his tongue. She gave a low groan of surrender and let her head fall back against his arm, opening still more, guiding him deeper. He began a slow, intoxicating rhythm, a rhythm she recognized; her body's throbbing timed itself to it so that it took over her awareness, became her only existence. She floated on that rhythm, rode the exhilarating crest of it, until at last she tore her mouth free and gasped, "Michael—I can't—I'm going to fall."

"No, I've got you," he growled, and swung her up into his arms. And then he stopped, looked down into her eyes and said softly, "I won't let you fall, Brady. I'll never hurt you again."

There was a sheen of sweat on his forehead, lines of strain in his cheeks. She lifted a hand to his face, tracing the lines, smoothing them with her fingers. Tenderness banished the sudden panic that had engulfed her and brought instead a sweet, sensual lethargy. Smiling, she touched his lips with her fingertips and whispered, "I know."

He carried her into the bedroom and, standing beside her bed, lowered her feet to the floor. With one knee on the bed, she put her arms around him, then moved her hands to the waistband of his slacks.

"In a minute," he whispered, and laid her carefully down, bending over her to give her a deep, drugging kiss. Against her mouth he murmured, "I'm trying so hard to take this slow and easy. I think I'll have a better chance of that if I keep my pants on."

Brady's breath broke up into slivers of laughter. "Is that what they mean when they say, 'Keep your britches on'?"

His soft gusts of laughter joined hers. "I guess it must be," he said, trying to remember whether he'd ever had occasion to laugh in the middle of lovemaking before.

"Oh, Michael," she whispered, beginning to shiver. "I don't know how much more of this I can stand. It almost scares me."

"Believe me," he said, smiling tenderly down at her, "it scares me, too." He straightened and reached to turn on a lamp beside the bed, then stretched himself alongside her and combed her hair back from her forehead with his fingers. "But it's better lying down."

"Uh-huh." She captured his hand and, bringing it to her mouth, began to do to his hand what he had done to hers. Making her words warm, moist puffs that sent shivers scooting up his arm, she whispered, "This way you don't have to worry about your partner keeling over in the middle of things."

Laughter shook him, filling him with warmth and tenderness and that peculiar champagne effervescence. He watched her face while she made love to his hand and thought he'd never seen anything so beautiful. He watched her pink tongue flirt with the crevices between his fingers, watched the shape her lips made as she took each finger into the sweetness of her mouth, and felt something inside him grow hot and tight....

When she had done with that delightful torment, she carried his hand downward and laid it on her breast, arching into it, making her body a silent request. He answered it, chafing her nipple with his damp palm, shivering it to aching tautness with her own moist essence. When it was pebble-hard again, he covered it with his mouth and gently warmed it, then pulled with strong, rhythmic tugs that caught at something deep in the core of her body. She moaned softly and pulled one knee up, squirming a little, beginning to fight against the sensations in her body that frightened her. The lower part of her belly and the spot between her legs felt hot and swollen, and every heartbeat seemed to hammer in those secret places.

He lifted his head and ran a gentling hand down across her ribs to the taut muscles of her stomach. "Easy," he whispered, smiling at her. "Don't fight it. Just let whatever happens, happen. It's only loving."

She smiled and said, "Oh," and tried to open her eyes, but her eyelids were too heavy. Her belly moved against his hand, and he began to make slow, circling strokes, dipping under the lacy edge of her panties with each pass. She sighed, trying to relax, and reached up to pull his head down to her breasts. Arching her back slightly, pushing against the pressure of his mouth, she burrowed her fingers into the cool, crisp silk of his hair, then buried her face in it.

She hardly noticed when his mouth left her breast and began to move downward, tracing the gentle rise of her ribs with open kisses, discovering the matte-velvet texture of her skin with his tongue, finding the spot just below her ribs where her pulse jumped against his lips like a wild thing. But when his tongue probed the delicate depression of her navel, she gasped and brought her hands to the spot in an automatic gesture of protection.

"It's all right," he said with his mouth against her skin. "It's only loving." Hooking his fingers in the silky material of her panties, he drew them down over her hips. Her belly muscles quivered under his mouth; her fingers touched his face, then stroked his hair with silent acquiescence. He lifted his head to watch his hand glide over the swell of her hip to the long, golden sweep of her thigh.

His hand slowed, then stopped; his breath hissed sharply through his teeth. "Oh, Brady..."

She touched his shoulder and said groggily, "It's all right. It doesn't hurt."

"I want to see it," he said thickly, and gently but firmly turned her on her side, facing away from him. First with his fingertips and then with his mouth, he traced the purple-and-blue mark, broad as the span of his hand, that marred the satin smoothness of her hip and thigh.

"That feels good," she murmured, moving sinuously against him. "Your mouth feels good."

His reply was wordless. With his mouth hot and open against her hip, he molded the rounded fullness of her bottom with his hand. She sighed and drew her leg up, granting him access to her feminine secret places. At first, when he slipped his hand into the hot, throbbing place between her thighs, she opened to him still more, but very soon she began to tremble, and her moans took on a desperate note. He turned her then and, putting his arms around her hips, pressed his face against her belly and held her tightly until the trembling eased.

"I know," she said, half laughing, half sobbing, stroking his head with her hands. "It's only loving. It's just..."

"I know. I know." He tipped his head down, pressing his mouth to the silky apex of her thighs. "Will you open for me now?"

"Yes." Her voice was a breathless gasp. "Only—"

"What?"

"I want to see you. Touch you."

That masculine chuckle rippled inside him. "One thing at a time."

She had thought she'd felt all she could possibly feel, that her body had given up all the sensation it could possibly give. She found that she was wrong. When he touched her with his mouth, she thought she would die. Sensation shot through her like silver daggers. She gasped, cried out, writhed against his hands, but he held her firm. Finally she shattered into a million sharp-edged fragments while he held her and absorbed her inner throbbing.

When he gathered her into his arms, she was sobbing uncontrollably. He held her, stroked and petted her, and her shaking subsided gradually into a kind of quivering lassitude.

Presently Brady drew a steadying breath and moved her face against his neck. "That's never happened to me before," she said. She sounded grumpy.

Michael fought back laughter and said solemnly, "After what you've told me, I should imagine not."

"I'm not sure I like it. It scared me."

"Oh, Brady." This time he let the laughter cascade through him and erupt in cooling puffs across her damp forehead. And he held her tightly, tightly. Because it had been something that had never happened to him before, either—and it had scared him, too. Why, he didn't know. It certainly wasn't the first time he'd ever held a woman in his arms while she trembled with release, but in some way he couldn't explain, even to himself, he knew that this was different. *Brady* was different.

Her hand was wandering again, down over his chest, his ribs and around to his belly. When it reached the waistband of his pants, it paused.

Michael nudged her forehead with his chin. "Still want to see and touch?"

She tilted her head up to look at him. He saw the tips of her white teeth, delicately restraining the quiver of excitement in her lower lip.

"Yes, please," she said politely.

He placed a kiss on the tip of her nose and murmured gruffly, "Feel free."

But thinking it, wanting it, saying it...and actually doing it, she found, were different things entirely. She felt shy suddenly. Awkward and uncertain.

"Um," she said, looking up at him, "I think I need help."

His chuckle was indulgent as he brought his hand to his waistband. She pushed it gently away. "No, not that kind. Just kiss me. Please?"

His eyes grew dark and soft with understanding. Without a word, he moved one hand to cradle her head and press her by slow, languorous degrees into his kiss. His mouth was hot and drugging, a potion that banished her inhibitions and sent feathery shivers of enchantment rippling through her. It also robbed her of strength and will, and after a few moments Michael broke the kiss with a gust of frustrated laughter.

"That's enough of *that*," he muttered, and rolled away from her. He stood up and in a matter of seconds neatly disposed of the rest of his clothes. He turned to find her watching him with glowing eyes.

"You *are* beautiful," she murmured, teasing him with her smile.

"You are crazy," he growled, leaning over her, bracing himself on his arms.

Laughing, she reached for him, tilting her face up, searching for his mouth. "Beautiful."

"Crazy..." He held himself away from her, tantalizing her with tiny nibbling kisses.

That intoxicating mouthplay grew in tempo and intensity, leaving no room for words, no time for breath, until they were forced to stop, panting like boxers between rounds. Michael lowered his head and, with a groan, took one dusky nipple into his mouth while Brady, sighing, buried her face in his hair. He felt her hands on his back, feathering down his spine, gliding over his buttocks, then moving to the hard ridges of his pelvis. He felt her fingers slide slowly inward, and she finally touched the mat of springy hair below his abdomen, he murmured, "Chicken," and carried her hand to the part of him that ached for her touch. With his mouth feeling like cotton wool, he managed to say, "Don't be afraid."

"I'm not." Her lips curved into a tremulous smile. "Well, maybe a little."

"Small wonder." His smile was rueful, and the look in his eyes tore her heart. "I haven't treated you very gently."

Once again Brady felt a great surge of protective love. It made her forget everything except the need to erase the look of regret from his eyes. It made her forget her shyness, made her feel fierce and strong. "Michael," she said, her voice shaking, "you feel *good*. I love the way you feel. I'd love—" she drew a shuddering breath, "—to feel you inside me."

The bright glitter of pain in his eyes softened a little. A fan of creases appeared at their corners. "Brady, are you sure?"

"Of course I'm sure. I want you."

Smiling now, he gently shook his head and stretched himself alongside her. "All right, then, but not yet."

"Why not?"

"Because you're not ready for me. I'd only hurt you again."

"How do you know?"

He smiled at her belligerence and bent to nip her lower lip with his teeth. "I just know." His hand lay on her belly, idly stroking.

She tipped her chin up, reaching for his mouth, and at the same time began to move sinuously beneath his hand. "Then . . . make me ready."

"I will," he growled, and parted her lips with his tongue.

He took his time about it, though he was hot and aching with his need of her. He wanted her heated and honeyed, molten and sweet; he wanted to immerse himself in her as if in a pool of liquid enchantment. He wanted her shivering, mindless, sobbing his name....

"Michael, please." Her breath was sharp and shallow; the pressure inside her left no room for air. And yet—and yet she felt hollow, empty. She needed him filling her, wanted his hands bruising her, his mouth leaving marks on her skin. She needed his strength inside her, his heat engulfing her, his weight bearing her down. "Michael," she cried, "I need you. You won't hurt me. Please." She half raised herself, nipping his shoulders, raking his skin with her teeth, pressing her fingers into the resilient muscles of his back. "Please."

He held himself very still, looking down at her, stroking the hair back from her damp forehead. The skin under his eyes looked bruised. Brady touched his face with shaking fingers. Through desperate, whimpering laughter she said, "Michael, you won't hurt me."

Laughing shakily himself, he said thickly, "How do you know?"

"I just know."

With a sigh he closed his eyes and slowly lowered his mouth to hers. His tongue filled her, became part of her. So caught up was she by the mastery of his mouth that she didn't even notice at first that he had shifted them both so that he lay back against the pillows with her supple and pliant on top of him.

When she discovered the change, she gave a pleased little chuckle and wriggled closer to him, fitting herself to him. He said, "Do you like that?" When she nodded, he reached down to the backs of her thighs and drew them gently apart. He caressed her buttocks and thighs, relaxing her, then brought her knees forward. When she was astride him, open to him, he captured her hands, held them against his chest and said raggedly, "Then . . . you take control."

She gazed at him, eyes confused and passion-glazed. He closed his and gave a gravelly laugh. "I promised to be gentle, but I don't think I can. So I want you to have control. Understand?"

She shook her head. "I trust you."

With a groan he carried one of her hands to his mouth and pressed a fervent kiss into its palm. "I don't. I'll guide you, but you set the pace. Take as much of me—or as little—as you want."

"But I want all of you."

"*Brady . . .*"

Chapter 13

It was different that time," Brady said. "Better."

This time her sobs had been mixed with laughter, little shuddering ripples of joy. Now she lay draped across him, as sensual and indolent as a cat. Michael kissed the top of her head and murmured, "How?"

"How different, or how better?"

"Both."

"I don't know, just different." After a moment of thoughtful silence she laid her hand on her stomach and said in a voice filled with awe and wonder, "Michael—I felt you in *here*."

He swallowed a chuckle. "That's what you get for being greedy." His hand lay on the damp mound at the juncture of her thighs, his fingers protectively covering her femininity. He could still feel her body's intermittent pulsing, aftershocks of the turbulence that had shaken her moments before.

She drew a shaky breath and put her hand over his, holding it tightly to her body. "Last time I felt like I was breaking apart. This time it was like an earthquake deep inside. But with everything *together*. Because you were with me. It felt *good*."

"I'm glad," he said huskily. "But it's always different. It might not be anything like that next time."

"Oh." She raised her head to look at him, smiling. "Always different?" He nodded. She gave a happy chuckle and put her head down on his shoulder. "I guess that's why people keep doing this, huh? It never gets to be a drag."

A sardonic snort escaped him unexpectedly. Something hot and scratchy sat heavily in his chest. "Oh, Brady, believe me, when the person and the circumstances are wrong it can still be a drag." He rolled away from her abruptly and sat up, then looked back and reached out to touch her cheek in mute apology. "Back in a minute," he muttered, and left her.

Feeling chilled and abandoned, Brady propped her head on one hand and watched Michael walk into the bathroom. There wasn't much left of his armor, but he had gathered what there was around him before his retreat, like a battered knight leaving the jousting field to regroup.

She heard the water running. A few minutes later Michael came back with a warm, wet cloth. When he sat down beside her and began to bathe her, she reached up to touch the lines of strain beside his mouth.

"Michael," she said softly, "who hurt you?"

He looked up, fixing his startled eyes on hers. "Hurt? I haven't been hurt."

She sighed and lay back, giving herself up to his tender ministrations, thinking about the contrast between his gentleness and the rock-hard lines of his jaw. Hurt? Oh, yes—and disillusioned, too. Who did this to you, Michael? she wondered. What made you take all your warmth and tenderness and fun and mischief and wrap it in armor? What made you afraid to be vulnerable? What made you afraid to love?

She wasn't going to let him get away with it, though—not this time! His armor was already a shambles, and she was a ruthless fighter when she had to be. So, looking at his averted face, daring him to meet her eyes, she persisted, "Well, somebody's soured you on the whole idea of..." She hesitated, and for the word *love* substituted "relationships. Who was it? Your wife?"

Michael shrugged evasively, then looked at her and gave a dry snort of capitulation. "Brady, nobody 'did' anything to me—unless it was me. What happened to my marriage was no more Helen's fault than it was mine. Probably it wasn't anybody's fault. No one sets out to destroy a relationship. Most people try to do the right thing. They think they're making the right decisions at the time." His mouth twisted with a bitter little smile that wrung at her heart. "Sometimes they find out they were wrong."

"Tell me about it. Please."

"Brady, do you really want to hear about my marriage?"

He sounded weary, but she was merciless. "Yes," she said firmly. "I do." And then, because the sadness in his face made her throat ache, she added softly, "Unless it hurts too much."

He shook his head and leaned over her to put the washcloth on the nightstand. "It doesn't hurt. It doesn't make me feel good, but it doesn't hurt. It's been a long time." Calculating the years, he stretched out beside her, then said in some surprise, "Five years. Incredible."

Brady snuggled into the curve of his arm. "What happened?"

"Nothing very dramatic—well, I suppose it was a little dramatic the day she told me she was leaving. But it wasn't really a surprise. At least it shouldn't have been."

"But it was," Brady said softly.

"Yes. It was. I don't know why. Catastrophic changes always come as a surprise." His voice was cool, analytical.

"But the marriage had been dead for years, and its demise was a gradual thing. I think the best way to describe it would be starvation."

Brady shivered. "That's horrible."

He shrugged. "I guess maybe it is. Sad, anyway. But, Brady it happens all the time. There's nothing unusual or even very interesting about my story, really. People marry for the wrong reasons, and then at some point down the road discover they haven't got anything to base a long-term relationship on. Things like common interests, mutual respect, friendship."

"Why *did* you get married?"

"I thought she was what I wanted," he said simply. "We met in college—and in those days lots of girls were still going to college to get their MRS degree. Helen was looking for husband material, and for some reason she decided I was it. As for me, well, it was a great ego booster to have the prettiest girl on campus on my arm. And...there was a certain amount of chemistry between us." He gave another dry, humorless laugh. "Unfortunately, we didn't find out until after we were married that the chemistry was fraudulent. We really weren't all that compatible after all."

He was silent. Brady rubbed her hand over his chest and let it rest on his belly. "You never had children?"

"No. At first we agreed that children should wait until I was through law school and established in practice. After that, Helen wanted to take classes, get her advanced degree. By the time we figured we were in a position to become parents, we'd discovered that we didn't really like each other very much, and I guess we just never wanted to confront the issue. We just drifted farther and farther apart, and then, after I was appointed to the bench, my life had so much pressure and stress in it, I guess I shut her out entirely. She says I did."

Brady nodded, and again found herself shivering. She could see him doing that—closing himself in, walling himself off, putting his armor on. "What I don't understand," she whispered, "is why did you stay married so long? If you knew..."

Michael shrugged and pulled the blankets up to cover them both. "It was comfortable. We were always very polite, very civilized with each other. We entertained now and then, provided each other with an escort when we were required to appear at public functions. I suppose if I'd had any compelling reason to end it, I would have. As it was, she found a compelling reason first."

"Someone else?"

"Uh-huh." After a long silence he said matter-of-factly, "She lives in San Marino now. As far as I know, she's very happy."

"And you, Michael?" Her voice was barely audible. "Are you happy?"

He didn't answer her.

After a long time, when he knew that she was asleep, he went to the living room and cleared away the dinner things. When the dishes were dried and put away, he turned off the gas log, blew out the candles and crawled back into bed beside Brady's warm, naked body. But he didn't sleep.

He should have been tired after such an eventful series of days. But he found himself staring wide-eyed into the darkness, listening to the sounds of the sleeping woman beside him and letting his mind run in aimless circles.

Talking about his past failures had depressed him. His mind kept doing instant replays of things he'd said. Those and other thoughts chased each other through the lonely corridors of his mind like players in a bedroom farce.

The right decisions... wrong reasons... thought she was what I wanted... Brady's different... chemistry... friendship... interests in common... Brady's too different... somewhere down the road...

He'd never thought of himself as having trouble with decisions. Making up his mind and facing the consequences was what he *did*. But somehow it was different when the decisions applied to his own life. He'd made one very bad one and had lived with its consequences for too many years. After that he'd found it easiest just to avoid getting himself into situations that required personal decisions.

Then he'd bumped into Brady Flynn, and she'd changed everything.

His life had been comfortable, orderly, busy. But now he wasn't sure of anything anymore. He didn't know how he felt about her or what he wanted, from her or even from his own life.

What about you, Michael? Are you happy?

He'd certainly been content.

He liked Brady—a lot. Liked being with her. She made him laugh, made him feel young and free, strong and wise. Making love with her had been incredible. He wanted her— in his bed and, yes, in his life. But for how long?

Brady loved him. She deserved a long-term commitment, not a day-by-day affair. But how could he give that to her when he didn't see how their relationship could possibly survive the long haul? He'd known her less than a week! They had virtually nothing in common. Chemistry wasn't enough; he knew that all too well. How could he tell whether what they had would grow into the kind of solid friendship that would survive the tough times?

The answer, he knew, was simple enough—he couldn't. It was a gamble. A risk. And the truth was he just didn't know whether it was a risk he wanted to take.

When the darkness had thinned to a translucent gray and he knew that dawn was imminent, he eased himself away from Brady's warm, firm body and tucked the covers snugly around her. In the bedroom next door he dressed in a pair of Sean Flynn's sweats and his own shoes, tiptoed through the house and slipped out into the morning.

It was foggy and wet with a cold coastal drizzle. Michael welcomed the sharp-edged chill; maybe it would help tone his body, at least, if not his head. Now, as at no other time in his life, he needed to keep himself fit, his mind clear. He couldn't forget that he had other decisions to make—decisions that would have consequences just as important as what he opted to do with the rest of his life.

He struck out down the hill, avoiding the trail that would pass the place where he'd been with Brady yesterday. He didn't like to be reminded of that. So instead he took the path he and Brady had followed in the rain the day they'd gone "a-borrowin'" to Mrs. Wu's.

As he was passing by the Wu's driveway, Mrs. Wu came out to pick up her morning paper, stately as an empress in a purple-red-and-gold caftan.

He called "Good morning," and she responded with the same open-mouthed surprise and delight with which she'd greeted Brady that memorable Saturday morning.

"Michael? Michael—how nice to see you! You're out early. Where's Brady?"

"I left her asleep," Michael said, wondering if he was compromising Brady's reputation in the neighborhood. He knew no one paid much attention to who cohabited with whom these days, but still, these were her neighbors, people who had known her since childhood.

However, Mrs. Wu merely nodded and said, "Brady never did like to get up early in the morning. Now me, this is my favorite time of day."

"Mine, too," Michael said, feeling just a little more dismal at the discovery of yet another incompatibility.

"Well," Mrs. Wu said, "I'm just about to go in and have a second cup of coffee and some cold spaghetti for breakfast. Care to join me? I *know* you must be dying for coffee. Brady doesn't believe in the stuff—which is probably wise, considering how bad it is for you."

"Well..."

"Come on, I'd love the company. Oh, damn—my newspaper's wet again." She picked it up, slapped it against her hip and, hooking her arm through Michael's, began to stroll with him up the driveway. "Wu won't be up for hours. He doesn't have to be at school until noon. He likes to work late and sleep in."

Michael glanced down at her, searching her face for signs of annoyance, but saw only serenity. Mrs. Wu looked up at him and smiled.

"Oh, it *is* nice to be able to look up at a man now and then." She chuckled and gave his arm a squeeze. "What a shame to waste all that height on Brady!"

"Mrs. Wu," Michael said thoughtfully, "do you mind if I ask you something?"

"Of course not. Ask away. And please call me Nancy. Brady's known me since she was in diapers, so to her, Mrs. Wu is just my name. But I do have a first name, and most of my friends call me by it."

"Thank you," Michael murmured solemnly. "I'm glad you consider me a friend—considering this is only the second time that we've seen each other."

"Oh, I generally make decisions about people pretty quickly," Nancy Wu said placidly. She had led him around the house to the back door, and he held it open for her while she picked up two plastic bottles of milk from the steps. "I told Brady she could trust you." Going through the doorway, she paused to give him a wink. "Should I have?" At the expression on his face she broke into her rich, mellow laughter. "Never mind, Michael—I'm teasing you. Sorry. By the way—" she set the milk bottles on the kitchen counter and turned to him "—now that you know my first name, do you have a last name? Not that it matters, I was just curious."

"Snow," Michael said. "Michael Snow."

"Ha." Mrs. Wu looked down at the rolled-up newspaper in her hands. "Brady told me you were in law," she said as she began to strip the rubber band from the paper. "I just assumed she meant a lawyer." She carefully unrolled the damp paper and spread it on the table. When she looked back at Michael, her gaze was direct and shrewd. "You aren't, are you?"

"No," Michael said. "Not anymore."

"That's what I thought." She held out her hand. "Judge Snow, I am so *very* pleased to meet you. Now come sit down and let me pour you some coffee. Care for some cold spaghetti?" Michael let out his breath with a gust of comfortable laughter. "I'd love it."

Mrs. Wu's kitchen was bright and warm, and it smelled of coffee and tomato sauce and spices. Looking around at its potted plants, copper pots and cheery knickknacks, Michael realized that he felt as if he'd known her for years. And he also realized that in two short meetings with Nancy Wu he'd already discovered he had more in common with her than he had with Brady.

"Now then," Mrs. Wu said when she had settled them both with mugs of steaming coffee and huge bowls of sticky red pasta. "What was it you wanted to ask me?" She gave him a perceptive glance. "You look like a man with something on his mind—besides gangsters," she added, patting the newspaper.

Michael cleared his throat. "It's a personal question."

Mrs. Wu spread her hands. "I'm a blabbermouth. Ask."

"I've noticed that you and Mr. Wu don't seem to have very much in common."

"Hah!" She gave a spurt of laughter and shook her head. "Nothing—absolutely nothing. Except, of course, thirty-four years of marriage."

Michael stared at her. "How did you do it?" he asked bluntly.

Mrs. Wu smiled at him. "We *like* each other's differences, Michael. I've never tried to change a hair of Wu's balding little head—never wanted to—and he feels the same about me." She thought for a minute, and Michael saw her eyes take on a softer glow. "We complement each other. He keeps me firmly attached to the ground, and I keep him from atrophying. It's a matter of mutual enrichment. Look, Mike.'' She reached across the table and put her hand on his. ''Are you worried about you and Brady? Because you think you two don't have anything in common? Let me tell you something. You want sameness? Look at the Sunshine Twins—they're practically clones of each other. That would bore me to death, drive me crazy. It's not a matter of how many differences there are between you, it's how you accept each other, same or different. If you're thinking about changing Brady, forget it. Do her a favor and get out of her life. Okay?''

She sat back in her chair, her dark eyes blazing. Michael looked down into his coffee. After a moment he said, ''I don't think I'd want to change her.''

''Mike,'' Mrs. Wu said softly, ''love and enjoy each other, just as you are. It'll work out okay. Trust me.''

Brady had tried not to panic when she awakened to find Michael gone, his place in her bed cold and empty. She'd been somewhat reassured to find his clothes lying where he'd left them the night before. So he wasn't *gone*, he'd just gone out. He'd be back. It's okay, she told herself. He's just an early riser, and he didn't want to wake me. It was really considerate of him to let me sleep.

So why was it that the sorest place in her body this morning seemed to be the region called the heart? And why was it that the thing about last night that had made the deepest impact in her memory was the terrible, sad story of Michael's marriage?

At least, she thought, though it was small consolation, I understand him better now. His marriage explained so many things.

She stretched and sat up, then got out of bed and walked into the bathroom. She brushed her teeth slowly, absently, while the bathroom filled up with steam. And all the while her thoughts wandered along their own paths.

No wonder he's afraid to try again, she thought as she stepped into the shower.

In a flash of early-morning insight she suddenly knew that his fear had very little to do with her. It was himself that Michael couldn't trust. He didn't trust his own judgment. It occurred to her that it was ironic—a judge who didn't trust his judgment. It was almost funny, except that it *wasn't*.

And the terrifying thing about it was that there wasn't a thing she could do but wait for Michael to come to terms with his own feelings, in his own way and in his own time.

"Hi," Michael said, pulling back the shower curtain.

Brady's heart began to pound. With water dripping from her eyelashes and sluicing off the end of her nose, she managed a hushed, "Hi." And then, glancing down at his sweats, she asked, "Have you been jogging?"

"Not exactly." His smile was wry. "I could use a shower, though. Is there room in there for me?"

Brady's heart took another crazy leap, and her mouth fell open. Before she could think to close it, Michael had skinned off his clothes and was stepping over the edge of the tub. In that small sterile space he seemed so *big* and almost overwhelmingly masculine. His body felt hard and cold— almost, Brady thought as his arms came around her from behind, like stone.

She shivered and murmured, "Mm, you're so cold."

"Not for long." He brought her against him and turned them both into the shower's spray. Covering her throat with his hand, he tilted her head up and back and leaned down to give her a lingering kiss.

When the world had righted itself again, Brady licked her lips and muttered groggily, "You've been to Mrs. Wu's."

"Yeah, I have. How can you tell?"

"You taste like coffee and tomato sauce."

"Sorry about that. We had cold spaghetti for breakfast."

"Oh, yuck."

"She sent you some."

Brady groaned.

His laughter was sympathetic. "That's all right; I'll eat it. You can have your Cookie Crackles cereal—or whatever it was—and goat's milk."

"Mmm," Brady said, sliding her water-slippery bottom against him. "I think I'd rather have some more of what I had last night."

"Oh, you do?" Michael gave a rough chuckle. "We're going to have to do something about that appetite of yours, you know that?" He paused to take a lingering drink from the small reservoir at the base of her neck. Surfacing, he said regretfully, "But I don't think it'll be this morning."

"Why not? You'd like it, too, I can tell."

"Oh, yeah? Well, you're right, I would." Laughing, he wrapped his arms around her to put a stop to her wriggling. "But you, my lady, have got to be sore."

"Uh-uh."

"Liar." He rubbed his flattened palms across her nipples. Her breath hissed between her teeth. "See?"

"Yeah, but that doesn't count."

"Oh, yeah?" Gentle as the water, his hand glided over her belly and slipped between her thighs. She winced, then groaned in chagrin.

"I don't know why. I didn't notice it at all last night."

His chuckle was tender. "Never mind. You'll heal fast. Here—if you'll behave yourself, I'll let you wash me."

"Are you sure you want me to do this?" she asked innocently as he handed her the soap.

Seeing the gleam in her eyes, he grated, "It'll be an exercise in self-discipline."

She made it as difficult as possible for him, taking her time, running her soap-slippery hands over every inch of him, paying special attention to buttocks and thighs and taut masculine nipples. By the time she had finished, there was a dangerous light in his eyes.

"All right, witch," he growled as he took the soap from her hands. "It's my turn now."

And he paid her back ten times over. His big hands had magic in them; they turned her knees to warm water and her insides to soap bubbles. When he had done with her she could only pant, "Michael..." and turn blindly into his arms.

In the next instant a gasping shriek of outrage burst from her throat. Michael, with one deft twist, had turned the shower spray to cold.

"You're leaving, aren't you?" Brady asked quietly. She was sitting cross-legged in the middle of her bed, wrapped in an afghan, watching Michael dress. He'd redeemed himself somewhat for the cold-shower stunt by giving her a brisk all-over rubdown with a bath towel that had left every centimeter of her skin rosy and tingling. That activity had degenerated into general roughhousing that had ended with Brady pinned beneath Michael's body in the middle of her bed, arms spread wide, her laughter merging with his in breathless gales. Then the laughter expired, and it was their mouths that merged.

"Oops," Brady had murmured when she could speak again. "I think it's time for another cold shower."

"Brady..."

"Michael," she'd said seriously, "this can't be good for you—physically, I mean. Isn't it supposed to be—"

"That," Michael said sternly, "is a myth. Perpetuated by generations of adolescent males with overactive glands. Come on, you insatiable witch, let me up. It's time we both got our minds out of bed."

But Brady could see even then that Michael's mind had already left her. She cleared her throat and looked down at the hand that was busily plucking fuzzballs from the afghan. "Do you have to go?"

She heard the gentle expiration of his breath. "Yes, I think I do. I may not have an assassin on my back anymore, but there are still the Gianelli brothers. The trial resumes tomorrow. I have a decision to make regarding defense counsel's motion for mistrial."

Brady nodded, touched her throat, then cleared it. "Have you decided what you're going to do?"

"Yes. I have." The grim lines of his face softened into the faintest of smiles. "I just need to figure out the best way to say it. Come on, witch." He leaned over to give her a quick kiss. "Get dressed. You're coming with me. Are you forgetting what I came up here for in the first place? I need to take you to get your car."

Michael's own car, Brady discovered, was a Mercedes. The first thing he'd done upon discovering he was no longer the target of an assassin had been to have it released from police custody. The next thing was going to be to move back into his own home.

His own home. Brady looked at him when he said that, but didn't say anything. It gave her a funny feeling to think of Michael having a home—a real home. The apartment didn't count. He'd become so much a part of *her* life, yet so far she'd seen him only in the context of the part of his life that directly touched hers. Realizing that there were large sections of his life she'd never seen, didn't know about, was not a part of, filled her with inexpressible longing. She wanted to be a part of *all* the areas of his life. Every day. For the rest of her life.

It was a very bleak and lonely feeling, that awareness. Because she really didn't know whether Michael was ever going to let her share those areas of his life or not.

Her Jeep was in the parking lot where she had left it, looking dusty and abandoned, though it had only been there two days. It seemed like weeks.

Michael dropped her off, waited until she had the motor running, then rolled down his window and leaned out. "Will I see you in court tomorrow?"

His voice was curt, but there was a curiously defenseless look about his eyes. Brady forced a smile. "Wouldn't miss it. Of course, I'll be working."

He didn't answer her smile. "Meet me in chambers afterward, okay? We'll have lunch or something."

He waited for her nod, then rolled up his window and drove slowly out of the parking lot. Brady sat for a while in her Jeep, hugging herself against shivers that were a weird mixture of joy and vague, nameless fear.

"Guess who I saw riding up in the elevator," Kyle whispered as he slipped into the seat next to Brady.

"Who?" Brady asked dutifully, not looking up. She was busy putting a new set of pencils in order.

"Remember the spider-lady?"

Now Brady did glance up. "No kidding?"

"Yep, spider and all. Wonder what she does around here."

"Did you get up enough nerve to ask her for an interview?"

"It's not exactly the sort of thing you can do in an elevator, Brady. Besides, there's something—"

"*Shh.* Be quiet!"

The door at the back of the courtroom was opening. The bailiff got to her feet.

"All rise."

Praying that her legs would hold her, Brady stood. As the judge moved without haste to his chair, she thought of words like *imposing, dignified, godlike....*

The bailiff intoned, "Be seated and come to order." The judge leaned forward, adjusted his microphone and clasped his hands together in front of him. His glance swept the courtroom—the empty jury box, the prosecutor's table, the battery of defense lawyers, the packed spectators' seats.

Brady's heart cried, Michael, please look at me. Let me know you're there.

His dark gaze touched her once impassively and moved on. She found that her hands were shaking.

The rustlings and stirrings of anticipation and preparation gradually subsided. When silence had descended, the judge began to speak.

"Ladies and gentlemen, there is a motion before this court, filed by counsel for the defense, that these proceedings be declared a mistrial. I am now going to rule on that motion, but first I wish to make a few comments.

"In presenting its motion, defense counsel has argued that certain recent events in my personal life may have compromised my ability to render fair and impartial decisions in this case. In short, that I may have developed bias.

"First of all, there is no such thing as a human being without bias. Judges are human beings. Every man or woman who puts on judicial robes and goes to sit behind a bench brings to the position his own set of biases and prejudices. I readily confess to my fair share.

"I am, for example, prejudiced in favor of a rule of law—laws made by civilized and humane beings, not the law of the jungle. I am biased against those who break the law; against those who use violence, or the threat of it, to achieve their own ends; against those who prey on the weak, the vulnerable, the gullible. I am prejudiced in favor of the system of justice set forth by the laws of this country, this state, this city. And I am biased against those who attempt to thwart that system.

"Having stated my strong belief in the criminal justice system, I wish to state further that I will not allow that system to be held hostage by violence. If I do, I send a message to the predators among us that justice can be circumvented through threats and intimidation, and rule by law becomes rule by the gun. I will not send that message. Therefore, the motion is denied.

"Mr. Klineschmidt, is the state ready to present its closing arguments?"

"Yes, Your Honor."

"Your Honor, in light of this unexpected development the defense requests—"

The words droned on in a flat courtroom monotone—technicalities, routine requests, motions and denials. Brady didn't hear a word of it; she sat in a fog of love and pride until Kyle nudged her elbow and she discovered that she hadn't made a single mark in her brand-new drawing tablet.

"Hey," Kyle said. "Wake up. It's lunchtime."

Brady glanced at the clock on the wall in surprise. "It's only eleven o'clock."

Kyle shrugged. "His Honor packed it in early. Reconvene at two this afternoon. Want to fly to Acapulco for lunch?"

"Maybe later," Brady muttered vaguely and stood up.

The bailiff barely glanced at her as she walked by. At the door to the judge's chambers, she raised her hand to the wood panels, then hastily shoved her tablet and pencils into her new shoulder bag, wiped her palms on the front of her skirt and knocked.

Michael had already taken off his robe; he was just shrugging into his jacket as he pulled the door open.

Brady said, "Hi."

Michael said, "Hi. Come in." He looked at her the way a starving man looks at a banquet table.

"Michael, you were—" But her own hunger must have been obvious in her eyes, because suddenly his arms were around her and he was lifting her off the floor, kissing her and laughing and kissing her again. Giddy with love, she could only close her eyes and hang on tight, like a child on a merry-go-round.

When the spinning stopped Brady sighed and murmured, "Oh, Michael, I love you."

"Brady," Michael said, hugging her hard. And then, huskily, he went on, "Hey, let's get out of here, and get some lunch. Someplace where we can eat outside. I need fresh air!"

"I know a place," Brady said. "Over at the Music Center."

The assassin was breathing hard when she slipped into her rooftop hiding place. She had to waste precious moments regaining her composure, but her hands were steady when she picked up her rifle.

It had been a shock to see the people from the Gianelli trial in the cafeteria. They were early. The judge might already have left the courthouse. The girl had to be with the judge; her reporter friend had been lunching alone.

Disciplining herself to patience, the assassin scanned the street and mall area. The girl was wearing blue today—not an easy color to pick up from this distance. And the gun's telescopic sight was useless until she knew where to look.

There. There they were, near the tunnel to the Music Center. A look through the sight confirmed the target, but it was too late. She couldn't risk hurrying the shot; it had to be perfect, precisely placed. She had to be certain that the bullet would do just the right amount of damage.

She searched the Music Center mall with burning eyes until she had once again picked up the target. There she was, passing the fountain, heading toward the Ahmanson Theater. Once again the assassin considered the shot and rejected it. The angle wasn't right. The judge was in the way.

When her target entered the little outdoor café and sat down at a table, the assassin began to smile.

* * *

"What I'm dying for," Brady said, scanning the menu, "is a burrito. But it looks like I'll have to settle for a cheeseburger. And French fries. What are you having?"

"Fettuccine," Michael said, grinning wickedly. "With red clam sauce." Brady groaned.

She was wearing blue chambray today, Michael noted. A skirt with lace and eyelet embroidery and ruffles and all sorts of other things that he thought should have been appalling but weren't. She looked delicious and feminine and altogether fetching, and he thought he'd never tire of staring at her. Then she took out her pencils and notebook and asked if she could do a few sketches of him, because she'd been so awed by his speech that she hadn't done a single one in the courtroom. He laughingly agreed, just to have a good excuse to go on looking at her.

"Your expression's no good," Brady said sternly. "It's not dignified enough. You look like you're having fun."

"That's because I am."

"The station manager is never going to buy this. Do you want to get me fired? Come on, now—eyelids at half-mast, jaw like rock."

Michael made a horrendous face. "Like this?"

"Perfect," Brady said straight-faced, and began to draw.

Michael heard only a peculiar buzzing sound, as if a gigantic mosquito had zipped past his ear.

With excruciating clarity, in slow motion, he saw Brady's arm jerk as if a puppetmaster had pulled its string. He saw her pencil fly out of her hand and the box go crashing to the ground. He saw her mouth open, saw her lift wide, bewildered eyes to his.

In a high, shocked voice she said, *"Michael?"*

They both stared down at the bright red drops that were beginning to splash across the pages of her sketchbook.

Chapter 14

There were noises then, sounds that would stay with Michael for the rest of his life: the sound of his own voice ripping through his throat, shouting, "Down! Everybody—get *down*!" Explosions of shattering glass, and the clang of the metal table hitting concrete when he overturned it in his haste to get to Brady. Confused shouts and frightened screams. And the smaller noises, in some ways more terrible: the sound of his own heartbeat, like pounding surf inside his head; Brady's terrified voice whimpering, *"No...no."*

Covering Brady's body with his own, Michael lifted his head to shout, "Don't panic. It's a sniper. Stay down. Don't move." He spotted a white-faced waiter hovering in the doorway of the café and called, "Hey, man—can you hear me?" The waiter nodded. "Call an ambulance—the police. Dial 911."

"Already done," the waiter shouted back and started forward. "Hey, she hurt? What—"

"Stay back! Keep everybody inside!" Already he could hear sirens in the distance. "Help is on the way, sweetheart." His voice broke as he looked down into Brady's shock-glazed eyes. "Hang on, okay?"

In stark disbelief she said, "I've been *shot*."

"I know, I know." Fighting down his own rising panic, he managed to ask calmly, "Where did it hit you? Can you tell me?" It was so hard to tell. Blood seemed to be everywhere.

"I don't know. I can't—my arm feels numb." And then, in a high, stricken voice, "Michael, my hand—I can't feel my fingers!"

Kyle heard the sirens as he was about to leave the cafeteria on the top floor of the courthouse. He was making his way across the dining room to look out a window when his beeper went off. With a muttered, "Damn!" he changed direction and went instead to the pay phones in the elevator lobby.

"We've got a sniper situation in your area," the news director said when he came on the line. "The police monitor says shots fired, man down. General vicinity of the Music Center. Know anything about it?"

"Just heard the sirens," Kyle said. "I'm on my way. Get a Minicam crew and have 'em meet me there."

The Music Center mall was a hive of police activity. Uniformed officers formed an uneven barricade to keep back the curious, while members of the SWAT team wearing flak jackets spoke earnestly into walkie-talkies and fanned out into the nearby high-rise office buildings. The air thrummed with the beat of helicopter rotors.

On the street below, Kyle was facing the video camera. "One shot—that's all that was fired, according to eyewitnesses. But it struck and injured a woman sitting at a table in a sidewalk café. A thorough search of the surrounding area is under way, but police sources say they believe it was an isolated shot and that the sniper—whoever he may be—is long gone. We do not yet have the identity of the injured woman, nor do we know the extent of her injuries.''

He broke off as he saw the team of fire department paramedics coming down the stairs from the mall level. ''Hold it, guys,'' he said tersely, and ran to intercept the tall man following the stretcher.

Michael Snow turned on him like a wounded animal. ''Stick that microphone in my face,'' he snarled, ''and it'll have to be surgically removed from your ear.''

''Hey!'' Kyle shoved the offending instrument into his coat pocket and held his hands out, palms up. ''I'm un-armed—see?'' He stopped short when he saw the blood. ''Geez, Your Honor, what the hell happened to you?''

''I've been trying to keep a friend of ours from bleeding to death, that's what happened to me! You idiot, don't you know that's Brady in there?''

''Brady?''

''God—'' The judge lifted a hand as if to drag it through his hair, saw the blood on it and instead curled it into a fist. His face made as vivid a picture of rage and anguish as Kyle had ever seen, but he knew better than to call the camera crew. ''I thought it was over. I really thought it was over. I wouldn't have let her near me if I'd had any idea—'' He whirled suddenly on Kyle. ''Why the hell don't you get your sources straight? I thought you said the contract was off!''

''Contract? Are you telling me—''

''Of course I'm telling you! The odds of this being a random sniping are about the same as you getting hit by lightning in your shower! That was *my* bullet. Mine—do you understand that?''

''Hey,'' Kyle muttered. ''Look, man.'' He looked over at the ambulance. ''Uh, tell me—how bad is it? Is she going to be okay?''

Michael took a deep breath. ''Yeah, I guess so. I don't know how much damage was done, but the bullet got her in the right forearm. Lot of bleeding, maybe some nerve damage. She says her hand's numb.''

"Oh, geez," Kyle said, as the significance of that sank in. "Listen, where are they taking her? County USC?"

"Yeah, I guess so. I don't know." Michael looked distractedly toward the ambulance.

"Well, look, can I take you over there? You don't look like you're in any shape to drive."

Michael's face went dark with anger. "Boy, you don't miss a shot, do you? What are you going to do? Drag a camera crew into the emergency room? Why don't you give her a break?"

"Why don't you give *me* a break, huh? Brady's my *friend*—you got that? My friend."

There was silence. Michael looked down at the ground and rubbed mechanically at the back of his neck. After a moment he let out a breath and muttered, "I'm sorry. I guess I'm a little upset."

"Yeah," Kyle said. "That's okay." He cleared his throat. "Why don't I go get my car—"

"That's all right. I appreciate it, but I think I'll, uh—" He cleared his throat and looked away. "I think I'll ride over in the ambulance. Lieutenant Sanchez is supposed to meet me there. He'll see that I get back. Thanks anyway."

"Right. Okay, then, I guess I'll see you there." Kyle turned and walked over to the waiting camera crew. "Okay, guys," he said tensely. "Pack it in. Get what you've got back to the studio and tell our friendly director to expect me when he sees me. Tell him...*geez*." He paused to rub a hand over his face. "Tell him Brady's been shot."

"Hi, witch," Michael said softly. "How are you doing?"

Brady tried to smile. "To tell you the truth, I've been better."

"I know." He touched her cheek with the back of his fingers. Her skin seemed almost transparent. All at once he found that he was incapable of speaking above a whisper. "I'm . . . so sorry. This shouldn't have happened."

"Michael, it wasn't your fault." She sounded so breathy and weak—not like herself at all. "I'm just glad you're all right."

"*God* . . ." He covered his eyes with his hand.

"Michael," Brady said huskily, "would you do something for me?" He uncovered his eyes. "Would you please come here and kiss me? I want to touch you so badly, and I can't." Her injured arm was securely strapped to her torso; the other was attached to an IV.

Michael touched her lips with his fingertips, then leaned over and kissed her. When he pulled away, he left his hand on her forehead, lightly stroking.

She sighed and murmured, "Thank you; that's better. I don't know why they've got all this stuff. It's just my arm. I feel silly."

"They're treating you for shock," Michael told her gently. "It's one hell of a trauma, you know—getting hit by a bullet. Your body doesn't like it a whole lot."

"My arm's going to be okay, isn't it?" Her voice shook slightly. "I still can't feel my fingers."

"It's probably just temporary numbness. The paramedics didn't think there were any bones broken." He spoke firmly, with a confidence he didn't feel. "You're going to be just fine."

"Michael?"

"What?"

"I hope this doesn't mean you're going to stay away from me from now on, you know, for my own protection."

Michael closed his eyes, afraid to look at her, afraid to try to speak. He was closer to crying than he'd ever been in his entire adult life. Stay away from her? If only he had. If only he *could*. But the truth was he probably wasn't ever going to be able to stay away from her again.

Something had happened to him while he was sitting at that table watching Brady's precious blood make crimson patterns on her drawing tablet. Something that once and for all cut through the garbage and blew away the fog in his brain that had been fouling up his judgment.

He didn't know when or how it had happened, but he loved this woman. Loved her in ways he hadn't even begun to catalog. Loved her as he never had loved Helen. And he didn't give a damn whether they had anything in common or not. Who cared whether she liked Italian food or junk cereal! It didn't make any difference whether he'd known her a week or a year. Ten years. She was his friend and she was his lover, and he wanted her in his life—*all* of his life.

Now, if he could just get his life under control again so he *could* share it with her.

"Well," Lieutenant Sanchez said morosely, "it looks like we're back to square one."

"Oh?" Michael said sardonically. "And where is that? As I recall, that's nowhere."

Kyle glanced at them and paced a short distance, jingling his car keys. Sanchez snorted. Michael rubbed the back of his neck. They were all feeling the effects of that stupefying mix of boredom and apprehension that permeates hospital waiting rooms.

"Shh," Kyle said, though no one was talking. "Here she comes."

A wheelchair rolled silently into the room, propelled by a determinedly cheerful-looking nurse. Brady's arm was in a sling. She looked a little embarrassed.

"Can you believe this?" she croaked. "I have a sore arm, so they put me in a wheelchair."

"Hospital regulations," the nurse said cheerfully. "She's all signed out and ready to go. Is someone here going to see that she gets home?"

The three men looked at each other. Kyle cleared his throat and said, "I am."

Brady looked past him to find Michael with her eyes. He walked slowly over to her and touched her hair with his fingers.

"I have to get back to the courthouse," he said softly. "I wish I didn't. I'll be over as soon as I can."

She nodded without taking her eyes off his face.

"You just go to bed and rest, okay? Call Mrs. Wu if you need anything."

She nodded again, and he saw her swallow. "I'll be fine. I've got all this stuff I'm supposed to take—antibiotics and painkillers and I don't know what else. Don't worry about me. As they say in the movies, it's just a flesh wound." She smiled, but when he leaned over to kiss her, he saw the shadow of fear in her eyes.

"You know," Brady said with a testy sigh as she was being wheeled through the exit, "this is the third time in a week that somebody's had to take me home. Why do these things keep happening to me?"

Michael and Sanchez looked at each other.

"Are you thinking what I'm thinking?" Sanchez drawled a few moments later as the two men stood watching Kyle's car turn a corner and disappear.

Michael looked at him and frowned. "You mean, why *do* these things keep happening to her? Yeah, I thought about that. But that's crazy."

"Is it?" There was a quizzical light in the lieutenant's black eyes. "Let me tell you something. A long time ago, when I was still in the academy, I had an instructor. I don't even remember what for, but I remember he was an ex-combat marine, and I remember what he always used to say to us. He'd say, 'Men, once is circumstance; twice is coincidence; the third time, it's *enemy action*.' You know, I've never forgotten that."

He and Michael looked at each other in silence for a few minutes. Michael let out an exasperated breath. "Yeah, but who in the world would want to harm *Brady*?"

"I don't know," Sanchez said, frowning, "but I think we ought to go back to the station and look at what we've got, then see if we can come up with a new angle. Don't you?"

"Good idea. Except—damn!" He snapped his fingers. "It'll have to be a little later. I've got to be in court in—" He checked his watch. "Good Lord—ten minutes. Can you get me there?"

The light in Sanchez's eyes became a gleam. "Why do you think God put sirens in cop cars? Hop in and buckle up, Your Honor!"

"There now," Kyle said, plunking the phone down on the coffee table. "I think that's everything. Sure you're going to be all right? Need anything else?"

"I'm *fine*," Brady assured him for the third or fourth time. "Go on, get out of here. Stop fussing over me." He'd already waited around while she'd changed out of her bloody clothes and into a pair of sweats. He'd made sure she'd swallowed her first handful of pills, then he'd settled her on the couch, covered her with quilts, turned on the gas log and brought her the telephone. "Quit acting like I'm some sort of invalid." Though she had to admit that she felt a little like one—trembly and weak, the way she'd felt once after a long bout with the flu. And there was something else, not as easily defined. Though it wasn't a physical thing, if she'd tried to explain it she would have said it felt as if the floor had just dropped out from under her. Her sense of security was gone.

"Okay, you call Mrs. Wu if you need anything, you hear me? You want me to call her for you right now?"

"Kyle, for Pete's sake, I have one good hand; I can still dial a phone!" She stopped suddenly and squeezed her eyes tightly shut. Her voice degenerated to a squeaky whisper.

"Oh, Kyle, what am I going to do if I can't draw? What am I going to do?"

"Hey…" Kyle caught a tear with his finger before it could slide down her cheek. "What's this? What would your old man say? You're a Fightin' Flynn—and don't forget it. Okay?" His voice was gruff. Clearing his throat, he leaned over to plant a kiss on her forehead. "You're gonna be fine. Give it a little time."

"But I still can't feel my hand at all."

"What did the doctor say? That it was probably temporary nerve damage, right? Let it heal, get the swelling down, a little physical therapy, and it should be fine. And if it isn't they'll try surgery. Have faith in modern medicine. Have faith in *yourself*. You're a strong lady. Hey, I've gotta go. Take care. Promise me you'll be a good girl and stay in bed, okay?"

"If I'm such a strong lady, how come you're treating me like a baby?" Brady grumbled, but the front door was already closing on Kyle's chuckle.

The silence suddenly seemed very loud. Brady sat listening to it for a few minutes, but silence left too much room for thinking, and remembering. She reached with her good arm for the phone and punched in Mrs. Wu's number, then awkwardly lifted the receiver to her ear.

"Oh, damn," she muttered to herself. "The phones are out again."

"Okay," Sanchez said, "let's try taking the three incidents one at a time and see what we come up with."

They were in the lieutenant's office. Sanchez had his chair tipped back and his feet up on his desk. Michael was pacing. "Okay," he said. "Shoot."

"Start with that hit-and-run. Tell me what you remember."

"Uh, Friday night. It was raining. We'd just started across the street. Brady had to jump over the water in the gutter. I remember she almost fell. That's about the time I noticed the car heading right for us."

"Stop right there a minute. Were the two of you together when the car aimed for you? Could the car have been aiming at Brady and not you?"

Michael considered, then rejected that with an impatient wave of his hand. "No, we were together. I had her by the hand, if I remember right—practically dragging her. It would have been pretty hard to hit one of us and not the other."

"Okay, okay. Let's skip that for the moment. I'm inclined to think it was a spur-of-the-moment impulse, anyway. It doesn't fit this lady's modus operandi. She's a sharpshooter, remember. As a general rule, specialists stick to their specialities." Sanchez thought for a few minutes, gently rocking himself on his chair's back legs. "Skip the mugging for now, too—we'll get back to it. Let's take today. Now the physical evidence suggests that the bullet came from the south or southwest. It hit Brady in the right forearm. You tell me what position she was in."

"Like this," Michael said, demonstrating.

"Facing southwest, right?"

"Right."

"And you were . . . ?"

"On her left."

Sanchez jumped up and came around his desk, dragging his chair. "Here—put the chairs the way you were sitting." When Michael had complied with that request, Sanchez came around to stand beside him. "Okay, if those chairs are facing the right direction, then I'm in the southwest, right? And you're in the south. How were you sitting? Forward, talking to her?"

"No. I was leaning back. She was doing a sketch of me." Michael smiled faintly. "I was supposed to look imposing."

"Tell me what you see," Sanchez said briskly.

"A clear shot," Michael said slowly, turning to look at him. "At either one of us."

"Me, too." The lieutenant was looking triumphant. "So if our sniper was any kind of a shot, how come she missed you and hit Brady?"

"Maybe she's not such a great shot. We've only got the word of Horner's street sources about that."

Sanchez looked thoughtful. "Horner swears by those sources. Let's assume for the moment that they're right. So let's assume the sniper attack was meant for Brady."

"But for God's sake, *why*?"

"Come on, Judge, that's easy. She'd recognized her the night of the hit-and-run, remember? Made a sketch of her, put it on TV. The girl can identify her."

"Come in," Brady called. "The door's open." Then it occurred to her that she probably ought to get up and open it, since it could only be a stranger. Everyone she knew would just knock and walk in. That was what most of her friends did, and of course Michael and Kyle knew she was supposed to stay in bed.

"Coming," she muttered, unwrapping herself from the afghan. She was just getting to her feet, pausing to let a wave of dizziness pass, when the door opened. She found herself staring openmouthed at the woman who stepped into the room.

She was quite simply the most elegant creature Brady had ever seen. She looked like a high-fashion model—tall, thin, with flawless olive skin and beautiful bone structure. She was wearing dark glasses, a camel-hair cape and matching turban, high leather boots and a great deal of exquisite antique gold jewelry. Brady noticed a large medallion in the shape of a lion's head, hoop earrings, bracelets and chains.

Brady closed her mouth, swallowed and said, "Excuse me—I didn't realize—um, can I help you?"

"Are you Brady Flynn?" The woman's voice was very deep and intriguingly accented. "The artist?"

"Yeah...oh! You must be the one the Sunshines told me about. Were you here the other day?" She had finally managed to get to her feet. "Sorry about all this," she muttered, feeling sloppy and frumpy next to this extraordinary woman. "I...um...had a little accident today. Please excuse the way I'm dressed—and the mess." She was fussing over the couch, sweeping aside magazines, folding the afghan. "My neighbors said you were interested in my work. Can I ask—" She turned back to the visitor, and the question faded away into shocked silence.

The woman had removed her dark glasses. Without them her face had a stark, gaunt look. Her eyes were black and very intense. As she stared into those eyes, Brady felt her world tilt and begin to whirl. A sense of déjà vu claimed her.

"Are you all right?" In the woman's polite voice Brady could hear the throaty rumble of a hunting lioness. "Perhaps you should sit down."

Brady carefully cleared her throat, testing her voice. "No—no, it was just a little dizziness, I guess. I'm still sort of weak." She tried to smile, but knew that it was too late. There was a cold half sneer on the woman's lips, a glitter of acknowledgment in the obsidian eyes.

The transformation was subtle but complete. The visitor's face was no longer beautiful or elegant or even exotic. It was simply the face of the assassin.

Kyle was sitting in his cubicle of an office, trying to work. He'd been letting research on his crime documentaries slide over the past few days, and he'd had an idea about doing some catching up. Instead, about all he'd done was sit there, tapping his teeth with his pencil, staring at the telephone. He'd been trying to call Brady all afternoon, but he kept getting a busy signal. It was beginning to irritate him.

"Hey, Kyle." One of the high school interns stuck her head around the partition and tossed an oversized manila envelope onto his desk. "The guy in the newsroom—what'shisname—said I was supposed to give you that."

"Okay, thanks."

"Sure thing." The girl popped her gum and disappeared.

Kyle pulled the envelope toward him and opened it. It was the blowup of Brady's sketch of the hit-and-run driver. He sat looking at it for a minute, then took a map pin out of a drawer, leaned across his desk and stuck the drawing up beside the one she'd done of the spider-lady. Still gazing at the picture, he sat down and tilted his chair back.

A moment later his chair hit the floor with a jolt that jarred his teeth. Swearing with all the virtuosity he'd picked up over the years from Brady's father, Kyle reached for the telephone and dialed the operator.

"Out of order?" he shouted into the phone. "What do you mean out of order? Are the lines down or what?"

"I'm sorry, sir," the operator's impersonal voice murmured. "We have no way of knowing that. We haven't had any other complaints from that area."

Swearing with real ferocity, Kyle looked up the number of the Rampart police station and dialed.

"I'm sorry," the switchboard operator said. "Lieutenant Sanchez isn't available. Is there someone else who can help you?"

"Look," Kyle said through his teeth, "it's vitally important that I reach Sanchez. Immediately."

"I'm sorry, but Lieutenant Sanchez is out on a case right now. I'm sure someone else—"

Kyle shouted, "He's got a radio, doesn't he? Damn it, don't you hear what I'm telling you? This is an emergency!"

"Sir, if you'll just calm down and give me your location—"

Kyle swore and hung up. "Don't panic," he muttered aloud to himself, then dialed Information.

The Wus were listed, which helped to calm him down a little, but when Mrs. Wu answered on the second ring his apprehension level skyrocketed. Whatever the trouble was with the telephone, only Brady's was out, and that was ominous.

"Mrs. Wu," he said tersely, "this is Kyle Horner. Do me a favor, would you, and go check on Brady? Yeah, I brought her home a while ago. She had a little accident today, and I'm kind of worried about her. Her phone seems to be out. Right—thanks a lot." He slammed the receiver down, snatched up his car keys and *ran*.

"All right, then," Michael said tensely. "Tell me this, why hit her in the arm? Why not in the head? Why not kill her?" His voice was rising; he knew his emotions were getting in the way of rational thinking. But he just kept seeing Brady lying in a pool of blood, all the magic and light gone from her eyes.

"I don't know," Sanchez said, glancing at him. "That purse-snatching, now. That doesn't make a lot of sense, either. There doesn't appear to have been any real intent to harm her. The hood just grabbed her purse and ran."

"None of it makes sense," Michael muttered in disgust. "That purse-snatching was probably just that—happens all the time."

"Remember," the lieutenant said severely, "we're acting on the presumption of enemy action. And if we do that, then every single incident must have a purpose. What we have to do is figure out what that purpose is."

"In the case of the purse-snatching, that shouldn't be difficult," Michael said sarcastically. "Generally the reason for snatching a purse is to acquire the purse."

"Or what's in it," Sanchez said slowly.

Michael stared at him. His heart gave a little lurch. "Brady carried her sketch pad in her purse. She had a great big one, just for that reason."

There was another long silence. Sanchez rubbed his jaw. "The sketch pad. Okay, but why? The sketch was long gone—it had already been on television, the whole bit."

"Yeah, and it didn't produce much in the way of results, did it? But what if there was another one—one Brady didn't know she had, one that was a lot more recognizable."

"What are you talking about?"

"Look..." Michael leaned his hands on Sanchez's desk to keep them from shaking. Without knowing why, he suddenly found himself filled with a terrible sense of urgency. "Brady drew all the time. Every time I looked at her in the courtroom she'd be drawing, even when there wasn't much of anything going on. People were her thing. Maybe she drew a picture of this woman without knowing who it was—" He stopped suddenly and straightened. "Oh, boy. You know what? She always did feel there was something familiar about that hit-and-run driver."

"I'd buy it," Sanchez said, shaking his head, "except for one thing. If our assassin got the sketch pad when she snatched the purse, then why not, as you said, kill the eyewitness? Why hit her in the arm?"

"What if she didn't get the picture?" Michael said. "What if it wasn't in the sketchbook?" His pulse was beginning to throb in his belly. He felt cold.

Sanchez frowned. "Where would it be, if not in the book?"

Michael snorted and made a distracted motion with his hand. "At her place, I imagine. It could be anywhere there. The place is cluttered with magazines, books, drawings, watercolors. Good God, man, do you know what this means?" He drew a hand across his face and turned on the lieutenant. His voice sounded like metal filings. "If we're anywhere near right, it means Brady's all alone out there in that godforsaken canyon of hers! She's a sitting duck.'' He felt as if he were strangling. "She doesn't even lock her door."

"*If* our hypothesis is right," Sanchez reminded him, trying to calm him down. "We've made a lot of assumptions. Don't jump to conclusions."

"Come on, Lieutenant!" Now he was shouting. "This is your bloody hypothesis. What are you going to do? Weasel out of it just when it starts to make sense? I've got to get out there—no, wait a minute. Give me the phone. I've got to try to warn her." He reached for the phone on the desk, then realized he didn't even know Brady's number. He wasted precious moments getting Information, praying she was listed. She was; his hands shook as he dialed the number. "Busy," he muttered a moment later. "I'll try the operator—emergency interrupt."

A moment later he was staring at the receiver in his hand, feeling cold all over. "The operator says there's no one on the line," he said. "She says it appears to be out of order."

Without a word, Sanchez stood up and reached for his jacket.

"Ah," the assassin purred, "I see that you do know who I am."

"Well, yes," Brady mumbled, desperately backtracking. "My neighbors told me you'd been by, asking about my pictures and, um..." She stumbled to a halt and turned away. It was just too terrible, looking into those cold, dead eyes. If she looked into those eyes she might become paralyzed by fear, like a bird in the thrall of a snake.

"I am interested in only one of your pictures, Miss Flynn," the woman said. "And I believe you know which one I am referring to—the one you did of me in the cafeteria."

"You're the spider-lady," Brady whispered.

The woman's laughter was like glass splinters. "Is that what you have called me? It was one of my best disguises—so simple, really. Most people never look beyond that silly little distraction." Her smile and her laughter vanished like lights winking out, one by one, in the windows of a house. "That you did, Miss Flynn, is your misfortune."

Brady licked her lips, but tasted only dust. Oh, God, she thought. Michael.... "But I don't—" She saw something ugly and dangerous take shape in the woman's face. Oh, Michael, she thought. I don't want to die. Especially not now. I've only just found you.

A footstep sounded on the front walk. Brady's heart jumped into her throat. The woman's eyes darted toward the door, assessing the danger.

"Hi, Brady," two slightly otherworldly voices said in breathless chorus. "We brought your milk. Can we come in?"

Chapter 15

"Can't you go any faster?" Michael growled.

"What do you want to do? Get me arrested?" Sanchez flicked a glance at him and muttered gruffly, "Sorry. Try to relax, Your Honor. We've got the sheriff's department and the highway patrol on it. Somebody should be there pretty soon." He flipped the radio's switch, picked up the hand unit and spoke into it.

There was a long pause before the dispatcher responded. "Sheriff's department reports units en route. Will keep you apprised of the situation."

Sanchez hung up the receiver and shrugged. "Guess all we can do now," he said softly, "is pray."

Oh, no, Brady thought. Not the Sunshines. Anyone else might have brought hope, the possibility of some kind of action, but the Sunshines, in their sweet, foggy innocence, were only a liability. Somehow she had to get rid of them before the assassin decided that they were a liability to her, as well.

But their arrival had done one thing for Brady. Like the snap of a hypnotist's fingers, it had jarred her out of her terrible, paralyzing fear. Her brain was functioning again. She was still terrified, but her adrenaline was flowing; she felt no weakness in her muscles, no pain in her arm at all. She seemed to vibrate with a strange kind of energy that was focused on one thing and one thing only: *survival*.

She was a Flynn. She wasn't about to give up without a fight.

"Oh, hi!" Sky and Shyla chorused happily when they saw the visitor. "I'm glad you came back," Shyla said. Sky nodded in agreement. "Have you seen Brady's stuff yet?"

The visitor growled a curt negative.

"I was just about to show her some things," Brady said.

"Oh, well," Shyla said with a breathless laugh. "I guess we better get out of the way, then."

Sky murmured, "Here's your milk," and held out the glass jar.

Brady cleared her throat and felt the assassin make an infinitesimal movement in response. She could feel that deadly presence like a coiled snake beside her.

"Um," she said, and held up her injured arm. "Would you mind putting it in the fridge? I'm sort of..."

"Oh," Shyla murmured, then gave a long sigh of sympathy. "What happened?"

Brady flicked her eyes toward the assassin and swallowed. "Oh," she said, trying a smile, "I just had an accident. It's nothing."

"Can we help?" Sky asked earnestly. "Shyla makes this herb salve. It really works great."

"It's very healing," Shyla added. "And we have lots of aloe vera, too. I'll bring some over, if you want."

"Thanks," Brady said. "Maybe later, okay?" Her face hurt from smiling.

"Okay." The Sunshines looked at each other; then Sky left to carry the milk into the kitchen.

The assassin's cold black eyes watched him until he was back at his wife's side.

"Thanks a lot," Brady murmured, and added hopefully, "Bye, now."

"Are you sure we can't do anything to help you?"

"Do you need anything?"

"We could make you some herb tea."

"Thank you," Brady said. "That would be nice." *Please God, just let them leave.* She could feel the assassin's anger and impatience like a physical presence. If they didn't leave soon...

"It was really nice seeing you again," Shyla said to the visitor. "I really like your medallion."

"You take care, now," Sky said gravely to Brady as he and Shyla finally made their exit.

Brady heard the soft hiss of the assassin's released breath. "Now then," the woman said coldly. "I have waited long enough. You will give me the drawing *now*, Miss Flynn." From the folds of the cape a gloved hand emerged, holding a small but efficient-looking gun.

Brady watched its stubby barrel come level with her midsection. She hugged her injured arm more tightly against her body and took a measure of comfort from the painful jab of the brass candlestick hidden beneath the folds of her sling.

It was getting on toward rush hour—the worst time of day to try to drive on the Pacific Coast Highway. Traffic was backed up at all the signals, and in one place, where the previous week's rain had brought down part of the palisades, the highway was restricted to one lane. By the time he finally made it to the Topanga Canyon turnoff Kyle was soaking wet with sweat.

He was negotiating a series of sharp curves at suicidal speed when he heard a siren. A few minutes later a sheriff's department black-and-white came barreling past him, red lights flashing. With a grimace and a fervent prayer, Kyle downshifted, pushed the accelerator pedal to the floor and followed.

Sanchez had turned on his red lights and siren when traffic on the Ventura Freeway got busy going through the Valley. He'd taken that route when the dispatcher warned him of the tie-up on the Coast Highway. Though he knew it was probably the quickest way into the canyon under the circumstances, it seemed to Michael like the long way around eternity.

"This woman really means a lot to you," Sanchez observed, relaxing a little as they left the last of the Valley's stoplights behind.

"You could say that," Michael said flatly. "I'm going to marry her." It didn't even surprise him to hear himself say it, though he hadn't known he was going to. *Please God— if she's still alive....* It occurred to him that he hadn't even told her that he loved her.

"Well," the lieutenant said, coughing a little, obviously uneasy with sentiment, "I guess I know how I'd feel if it was my wife."

"You're married?" Michael asked in some surprise.

"Yep," Sanchez growled. "Got four kids. You got any kids?"

"Not yet," Michael said, feeling as if his jaws had been wired together. "But I hope to." Brady's kids. Every one with her eyes and her sense of humor. And her guts.

The candlesticks had still been there on the coffee table, where she and Michael had left them. They'd been behind her, hidden from the assassin's view; it had been easy, while the assassin's attention was riveted on Sky, to slip one under her sling. It wasn't much of a weapon against a handgun, but it was better than nothing. Brady could only hope that she got the chance to use it.

"I am out of time and patience," the woman said. "You will give me the picture—now."

Stall. Wait for the right moment! Brady cautioned herself. She licked her lips. She felt her heart like a separate being inside her chest—something wild and out of control. "I would be happy to give you the picture. It's just that—" What should she say? If she admitted that she'd already given the picture to someone else, that it wasn't here, would it buy her time or get her killed on the spot? This woman was obviously insane; who knew how she would react? "I don't know where it is," Brady said finally, and added a helpless shrug. Rage burned hot in the assassin's eyes. The gun twitched slightly. "I mean," Brady added hurriedly, "it could be anywhere. I'd have to look for it."

"Look fast," the assassin hissed. "I will give you one minute before I burn this place down—and you with it."

The knock on the door stunned them both. Brady felt an absurd impulse to laugh. It was the last impulse she could remember with any clarity for a while, because what happened after that happened faster than she could think.

The door swung open, and Mrs. Wu sailed in, carrying a large stainless-steel kettle and trilling, "Brady, I've brought—"

But the assassin had already whirled and fired. The explosion had a strange metallic echo. With a look of surprise and outrage, Mrs. Wu staggered backward, clutching the kettle to her chest. As the sound of the bullet's ricochet screamed in her ears, Brady pulled the candlestick from its hiding place and brought it down across the assassin's gun hand. Both the gun and the candlestick went flying, disappearing into the jumble on the couch.

The assassin gave an animal snarl and turned on Brady with murder in her eyes. Brady took one reflexive step backward and held out a hand in futile defense. It was over now. She had no more weapons. Oh, Michael, I'm sorry, she said silently. It's not your fault.

And then Mrs. Wu drew herself up, screamed "Eee-*yah*!" and swung the kettle. It met the assassin's head with a sickening thud, and the woman dropped like a stone.

Echoes of violence screamed inside Brady's head like the cry of a thousand banshees. Her surge of adrenaline abruptly ebbed, leaving her feeling as if she was locked inside a shell of ice, unable to move, unable to speak.

Mrs. Wu moved first. Straightening from a half crouch, she looked from the woman on the floor to the dented kettle and back again.

"Oh, dear," she murmured. "I do hope I haven't killed her. It was only a pot of spaghetti, after all."

It was then that Brady realized it wasn't banshees she was hearing at all. It was sirens.

Michael and Lieutenant Sanchez were among the last to arrive. The suspect was in custody, although she didn't know it yet; she was still unconscious, having sustained what appeared to be a pretty severe concussion. An ambulance had been dispatched to the scene.

Kyle and two sheriff's deputies were talking to Mrs. Wu. She was explaining how her pasta pot had come to have two dents in it—one for her life, and one for Brady's. Two other deputies were already combing the woodwork, looking for the bullet.

Brady was sitting on the couch, turning a brass candlestick over and over in her good hand like a baton. Michael couldn't see her face; her hair was a wild, tangled mass, and for once she was making no effort to restrain it. It was almost, he thought, looking at the hunched, defensive set of her shoulders, as if she were hiding inside it.

He'd come up to the door slowly, almost fearfully, not because he was afraid of what he might see—he'd already gone through the trauma of relief down in the car when word had come through on the radio that Brady was all right. But he was a little afraid of what he might do. Emotional freedom was new to him; having his deepest feelings exposed in front of a roomful of people was still a frightening prospect.

Now, standing there in her doorway, he felt his need of her as a terrible burning emptiness inside him. With so much need in him he couldn't go to her, but instead just stood and drank in the sight of her, immersing himself in the wonder of her, like a thirsty man with a long, cool drink.

He hadn't moved or made a sound, but she must have sensed his presence, because she suddenly looked up. When she saw him, a light came on in her eyes. Sunshine... moonglow.

"Hello, witch," he said.

There was none of his fear and reserve in Brady. She uttered one strangled cry and launched herself toward him. He received her in his arms with tender care, because of her arm, and cradled her head against his heart while she sobbed. She hadn't shed a tear till that moment, he knew; her eyes had been clear and her cheeks pale but dry. He was glad she was doing it now. He knew she was probably going to have to do quite a bit more of it before the nightmares finally went away and she learned to feel safe again.

So he just held her, burrowing through her hair with his fingers, gently rubbing her scalp, stroking her shaking back. And after a while it seemed that her tears poured through him, too, like a cleansing flood, filling up the burning void inside him and overflowing. And as he stood there with his face buried in Brady's hair, he discovered that the roomful of people didn't matter at all.

He discovered, too, that his deepest feelings could be expressed very simply.

"Brady Flynn," he whispered brokenly, "I love you."

It was Christmas Eve. The Wus had come for dinner earlier, then had gone home. Brady and Michael were putting the finishing touches on the huge Christmas tree in Michael's living room. Not very many people waited until the night before Christmas to put up the tree these days, but it had been a tradition of Sean Flynn's. It was the way his family had always done it, and the way he'd always done it for Brady. And now, for the first time, Brady was doing it without him.

Now she was doing it with Michael. Life, she reflected, had a way of renewing itself, of constantly offering new gifts, new wonders, new beginnings.

She considered Michael her very own private miracle, and she knew, too, that she was his. He needed her. She had sensed his need of her long before he'd known of it himself. He'd trusted her enough to venture outside his armor, tentatively at first, but gradually opening up more and more. Now he rarely retreated back into his shell, and when he did, Brady never let him get away with it for long. All she had to do, when she felt him withdraw behind his dignity and authority, was to kiss him and say softly, "Come down off Mount Rushmore, George."

This was going to be a good Christmas, even though it was the first without Sean. The trial was over; the Gianellis and their business partner had been convicted on all counts. The appeal was in progress, but it was too soon to know whether Michael's controversial ruling would meet the test of the higher courts.

The assassin was gone, except for an occasional visit in Brady's nightmares, and those were coming less and less often. She had turned out to be a notorious terrorist from the Middle East named Simil Jihad, wanted on three continents. She had been extradited to France to stand trial for murder.

The only thing that kept it from being a perfect Christmas—except for Sean, of course—was Brady's hand. It was responding to therapy, but progress seemed very slow, and she couldn't help feeling frustrated sometimes.

Like now. Michael was doing all the work decorating the tree; all she could do was hand him things and offer advice. And when a beautiful crystal ornament slipped from her hand and broke, it was finally the last straw. She swore furiously and burst into tears.

"Hey," Michael said softly, coming over to wrap her in his arms. "Don't worry. It's only glass."

"I know—it's not that. It's my hand. It won't—oh, Michael, it's never going to work right!"

"Sure it will—if you want it badly enough. It just takes time, that's all." He took her hand and pressed a kiss into the palm, then began to massage it gently, manipulating each finger, carefully rotating the wrist. Brady sighed and relaxed against him. He touched her chin, and she lifted her face for a long, lingering kiss.

"Merry Christmas, Mrs. Snow," he whispered, smiling into her eyes.

"Is it after midnight?"

"Yup, sure is. Want your Christmas present now or later?"

"Now," Brady murmured, touching soft kisses to the front of his shirt. "And later...."

"Well, okay," Michael said judiciously. "Although that wasn't what I meant. Here..." He shifted her to one side long enough to take a small flat package out of his shirt pocket. "Merry Christmas."

Brady took it, curiosity gleaming in her eyes. He waited, holding his breath, while she opened it.

"Michael..." Her eyes were luminous with wonder and delight, like a child's. "I don't believe it. Season tickets to Dodger Stadium! But you *hate* baseball."

"Yes," he growled, lowering his mouth to hers. "But the point is, I love *you*."

"But—"

"Hush, witch. Don't argue."

"Or what?" Brady growled. "Will you hold me in contempt?"

"Never," Michael said fervently. "I'll hold you in love, in liking, in respect, in admiration...."

"Hush," Brady said. "For now, just *hold* me."

* * * * *

WOLF AND THE ANGEL

Kathleen Creighton

If you have enjoyed this story, you'll be
pleased to note that next month in

Silhouette Sensation

we will be publishing another
Kathleen Creighton novel.

Here's a brief preview. . .

WOLF AND THE ANGEL

Kathleen Creighton

"Excuse me."

The unexpected masculine voice gave Terry a nasty start.
She turned to look for the speaker and sighed inwardly when
she saw the man in the brown bomber jacket strolling toward
her, thumbs hooked in the belt loops of his jeans, teeth
showing white in an unshaven face. She recognized the type,
the over-confident grin, that certain almost-swagger in his
walk.

Since she didn't have either the time or patience to deal
with a man on the make at the moment, she wasted no time on
subtlety. She injected her voice with frost and snapped,
"Yes?"

The man gave one of those self-deprecating shrugs that are
meant to be just the opposite and drawled, "I don't know, you
looked like you had a problem. I thought maybe I could help."

Terry subjected him to a dismissive once-over, squinting
against the sun. "I doubt it—unless you happen to be a dentist
who speaks Spanish and flies."

"That sounds like some kind of riddle." The man chuckled, then held out his hands as if to say, Look, here I am—the answer to all your prayers. "Hey—two out of three ain't bad."

"Oh yeah, sure," Terry began, then gave the guy a second, longer look and ventured, "Which two?"

"Let's put it this way." He rubbed the bridge of his nose with a work-hardened forefinger; the grin slipped awry in a way even Terry had to admit was engaging. Sort of. "I don't think you'd want me poking around in your mouth . . . with sharp metal objects."

That did it. Any thoughts Terry might have entertained of changing her mind about the man evaporated. That tiny little pause, ever so subtly suggesting a double entendre . . . she really didn't need this. Not this morning.

Barely suppressing a shudder, she murmured politely, "I'm sure you're right. Now if you'll excuse me, I really do—"

"Have a problem. That's obvious. That's why I'm offering my services." A lean brown hand touched her arm. The voice became softer, deeper and slightly scratchy. "Listen, my Spanish is only fair, but I'm a damn good pilot."

In spite of her better judgment Terry hesitated. Something made her give the man another look, made her search his dark, unshaven face and finally meet his direct—and curiously intent—blue gaze. She saw nothing there to reassure her, nothing to make her trust his sincerity. In fact, she felt an odd uneasiness, a peculiar *quickening* inside, as if all her senses and instincts had just been turned up a notch.

The man, however, was apparently encouraged by her hesitation. He gave her a big friendly smile and looked as if he wanted to stick out his hand, but thought better of it. "My name's Jack, by the way. Jack Wolf. I'm a friend of Lee's—the blue-and-white Cessna over there."

He nodded to the businessman whose name she hadn't been able to remember. The businessman favored them both with a jovial smile and wave in return. The man who called himself Jack Wolf turned back to Terry, oozing charm—and that sincerity she'd been looking for—from every pore.

"You know, he's been telling me what you people are doing down there in Baja, and I just wanted to let you know, I think it's great. In fact, I've always thought about it—wondered what those people do, you know? For doctors, I mean."

"You have, have you?" Terry said acidly.

Careful, Wolf cautioned himself silently, don't lay it on too thick. This lady's no fool.

Abruptly changing his tactic, he answered the doctor's cynical gaze with an offhanded shrug. "Well, yeah, as a matter of fact I spend quite a bit of time down there myself—fishing, a little hunting—and it's occurred to me more than a time or two that if anything happened—you know, if I got hurt or sick or anything—I'd be up a creek, with the nearest doctor a couple hundred miles of bad road away."

He hooked one thumb in a belt loop, gave a casual wave and turned away. "Hey, listen, I didn't have anything pressing this weekend, and what you guys are doing sounded like fun, so I just thought maybe you could use another hand. But if you've got it covered . . ."

He could almost hear the battle raging insider her, the fight between the woman part of her that didn't trust him any farther than she could throw him, and the doctor part of her that needed him and knew it. But he never for a minute doubted what the outcome would be. Saints and do-gooders were all pretty much the same when it came to priorities.

Even so, she actually let him take three steps. "So—" she said in a loud, hoarse voice, then paused to clear her throat as if the words were hanging up there. "You say you're a pilot. Do you have a license?"

Wolf slowly turned. "Right here," he said, patting his hip pocket.

"Current?"

"Renewed last summer."

She stood there struggling with it for a while longer, chewing on her lower lip. For no particular reason Wolf suddenly noticed that, while the rest of her features were rather angular—prominent cheekbones, bold chin, arrogant, high-bridged nose—she had a very full mouth, with nice, soft lips. Definitely not the kind of mouth usually associated with saints.

"It can be tricky, flying in Baja," she said finally.

"Not so much flying as landing," Wolf remarked with a grimace. "Where you going? I hope not Colnett—geez, they've got these little tiny cactuses there that can play hell with your tires. And the airstrip at Punta San Carlos is apt to be half under water at high tide. Personally, I think that's better than trying to land on one that's been plowed under, but—"

"Dos Caminos," she said on an exhalation, a capitulation of sorts. "And then Santa Luisa."

Wolf put on his poker face and managed not to flinch. And all he said aloud was, "Not bad. Santa Luisa's a little narrow. How big is your plane?"

She must have told him, but he didn't hear her. He didn't give a rip how big her plane was, he'd have set a 747 down on that runway if she'd asked him to. It was better than he'd dared hope for, so good he figured it must have been Fate—or Luck, a lady he was always glad to have on his side. Here he'd been prepared to hijack the damn plane, or steal it if he had to, to get within striking distance of El Refugio de los Angeles, and now Fate was about to hook him up with somebody who could set him down within twenty miles of the place. And a medical team, yet. He couldn't have come up with a better smoke screen if he'd tried. Even if those two murdering Cruz brothers were watching their backsides—and with hit men on both sides of the drug war after them they were bound to be—the last place they'd expect retribution to come from would be a bunch of doctors and do-gooders.

"We're a volunteer group, I wouldn't be able to pay you," Terry said doubtfully, wondering whether she was trying to recruit the man or warn him away. She just wished she could make up her mind, one way or the other.

By all appearances—and disregarding *his*—the man named Wolf seemed like a godsend. Almost *too* good to be true, if he really knew Baja as well as he seemed to, and could manage even basic Spanish. For some reason she didn't doubt his ability to fly a plane; there was something, an aura of competence about the man that made her believe he could do pretty much anything he set his mind to.

But she didn't trust him. Oh no. Not any farther than she could fly that plane.

*   *   *

Wolf and the Angel is
an April Silhouette
Sensation. Don't
miss it!

Silhouette Sensation

COMING NEXT MONTH

WOLF AND THE ANGEL
Kathleen Creighton

Teresa Duncan knew Jack wolf was trouble the minute she saw him. Not for a second did she believe that he just wanted to help her get medical supplies to Baja, Mexico. Unfortunately, she needed him.

Jack's dangerous plans disintegrated a little more each day he spent with Terry. Soon he was just praying that he could keep Terry and the baby they'd been given alive. Revenge wasn't that important anymore. . .

JAKE'S WAY
Kathleen Korbel

She was everything he could ever want in life, but Jake Kendall knew Amanda Marlow would never be his. Jake's world stopped at his ranch's boundaries, whereas Amanda had the world at her feet. She would soon be moving on.

Jake Kendall was the most complex man Amanda had ever met. He spurned her at every turn, but she could see the longing in his eyes. What was it that held him back?

Silhouette Sensation

COMING NEXT MONTH

DESERT SHADOWS
Emilie Richards

Was rebellious Sister Felicia, the nun who stole cigarettes and went swimming in the nude, for real? Or was she a cool assassin, an impostor? Josiah Gallagher made his decision, but then he and the "sister" were stranded in the desert together, with only a slim chance of survival.

The desert trek told Gallagher all he needed to know about Sister Felicia, but there was no time to give in to passion. He was no saint and she was no sister, but they both had obligations to fulfil. Would they be in time?

HEAT LIGHTNING
Anne Stuart

Turner's Landing had never seen anything like Caleb Spenser. Handsome as sin and twice as mean, Caleb was rumoured to have killed a man. A smart person would keep out of his way.

Jassy Turner was usually coolheaded in a crisis, but nothing had prepared her for Caleb. He was like a fire in her blood and as dangerous as heat lightning. But what did he have against her family? Was he just using her?

COMING NEXT MONTH FROM

Silhouette

Desire

*provocative, sensual love stories
for the woman of today*

MARRIAGE TEXAS STYLE! Annette Broadrick
HONEY AND THE HIRED HAND Joan Johnston
ARROW IN THE SNOW Doreen Owens Malek
A ROCK AND A HARD PLACE Leslie Davis Guccione
DOUBLE TROUBLE Barbara Boswell
BLUE SKY GUY Carole Buck

Special Edition

*longer, satisfying romances with
mature heroines and lots of emotion*

CHERISH Sherryl Woods
IT MUST HAVE BEEN THE MISTLETOE Nikki Benjamin
A PRINCE AMONG MEN Mona van Wieren
WHEN SOMEBODY NEEDS YOU Trisha Alexander
JEZEBEL'S BLUES Ruth Wind
GYPSY SUMMER Patricia Coughlin

TAKE 4 NEW SILHOUETTE SENSATIONS FREE!

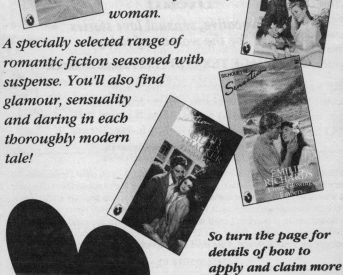

Silhouette Sensations are thrilling romances for today's woman.

A specially selected range of romantic fiction seasoned with suspense. You'll also find glamour, sensuality and daring in each thoroughly modern tale!

So turn the page for details of how to apply and claim more free gifts!

YOU CAN ENJOY 4 SILHOUETTE SENSATIONS, A CUDDLY TEDDY AND A MYSTERY GIFT FREE!

Yes you can enjoy 4 Silhouette Sensations as your free gift from Reader Service, plus the opportunity to have 4 brand new titles delivered direct to your door every single month!

You could look forward to receiving 4 Silhouette Sensations delivered to your door for only £1.85 each. Postage and packing is FREE! Plus a FREE Newsletter featuring authors, competitions, special offers and lots more...

It's so easy. Send no money now but simply complete the coupon below and return it today to:- **Silhouette Reader Service, FREEPOST, PO Box 236, Croydon, Surrey CR9 9EL.**

— — — — — **NO STAMP REQUIRED** — — — ✂

Please rush me 4 FREE Silhouette Sensations and 2 FREE gifts! Please also reserve me a Reader Service subscription. If I decide to subscribe, I can look forward to receiving 4 brand new Silhouette Sensations for only £7.40 every month. Postage and packing is FREE and so is my monthly Newsletter. If I choose not to subscribe, I shall write to you within 10 days and still keep the FREE books and gifts. I may cancel or suspend my subscription at any time simply by writing to you. I am over 18 years of age.

Ms/Mrs/Miss/Mr _____ EP47SS

Address _____

_____

_____ Postcode _____

Signature _____

Offer closes 31st October 1993. The right is reserved to refuse an application and change the terms of this offer. One application per household. Overseas readers please write for details. Southern Africa write to Book Services International Ltd., Box 41654, Craighall, Transvaal 2024. You may be mailed with offers from other reputable companies as a result of this application. Please tick box if you would prefer not to receive such offers ☐

mps
MAILING
PREFERENCE
SERVICE